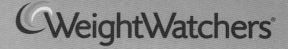

the
time to eat
cookbook

Over 300 new low Point recipes

Siân Davies

SIMON & SCHUSTER
A VIACOM COMPANY

First published in Great Britain by Simon & Schuster UK Ltd, 2002.
A Viacom Company.

Copyright © 2002, Weight Watchers International, Inc.

Simon & Schuster UK Ltd
Africa House
64–78 Kingsway
London
WC2B 6AH

Weight Watchers and Time to Eat are Trademarks of Weight Watchers
International, Inc. and used under its control by Weight Watchers (UK) Ltd.

Photography and styling: Steve Baxter
Food preparation: Carol Tennant
Design: Jane Humphrey
Typesetting: Stylize Digital Artwork
Printed and bound in Singapore

Weight Watchers Publications Manager: Corrina Griffin
Weight Watchers Publications Executives: Lucy Davidson, Mandy Spittle
Weight Watchers Publications Assistant: Nina Bhogal

A CIP catalogue for this book is available from the British Library

ISBN 0 74323 1309

Pictured on the front cover: (left to right) Spring rolls page 23; Summer fruit
gâteau page 184; Chicken lasagne page 64; Pad Thai page 47; Baked chocolate
custard pots page 165 and Pizza marinara page 93.

Pictured on the back cover: (left to right) Banana and nutmeg squares
page 189; Sweet and sour fish curry page 108; Summer berry pudding
page 171; Teriyaki turkey noodles page 129; Cannellini bean pâté page 14
and Roasted root cobbler page 81.

Recipe notes:
Egg size is medium, unless otherwise stated.

Fruit and vegetables are medium-sized unless otherwise stated.

Raw eggs: only the freshest eggs should be used. Pregnant women, the
elderly and children should avoid recipes with eggs which are raw or
not fully cooked.

Recipe timings are approximate and meant to be guidelines. The preparation
time includes all the steps up to and following the main cooking time(s).

POINTS You'll find this easy to read Points logo
on every recipe throughout this book.
The logo represents the number of
Points per serving each recipe contains.
The easy to use Points system is
designed to help you eat what you want,
when you want – as long as you stay
within your Points allowance – giving you
the freedom to enjoy the food *you* love.

(v) This symbol denotes a vegetarian recipe
and assumes that free-range eggs and
vegetarian cheese are used. Virtually
fat-free fromage frais and low-fat crème
fraîche may contain traces of gelatine so
they are not always vegetarian. Please
check the labels.

(Vg) This symbol denotes a vegan dish.

contents...

It's time to eat...
what you want, when you want

Are you looking for a flexible and straightforward weight loss programme, which totally fits in with your life? Then look no further! Weight Watchers' reputation for helping Members lose weight successfully is second to none. With the new Time to Eat programme it couldn't be easier. It's been designed to support and motivate you throughout the year, reflecting the foods, tastes and flavours of every season. You'll discover the benefits of healthy eating that Time to Eat gives you, from shaping up to feeling great, as you achieve your weight loss Goals.

With the easy to use Points system, you'll enjoy the freedom of eating what you want, when you want – as long as you stay within your Points allowance. It couldn't be easier – or more fun, especially when you drop a dress size, enjoying the foods you love!

The Time to Eat programme is there for you throughout the year. There are special monthly books and weekly cards to bring your diet and your daily life into balance. So, whether it's Mother's Day, Christmas Day, Pancake Day or St. Patrick's Day, there will be hints and tips for those special occasions to help you to have fun and still lose weight.

This cookbook has been written especially to complement the programme, with wonderful and inspiring recipes – all of them delicious, nutritious and low in Points. Welcome to the Time to Eat Cookbook – a fantastic book to support you on the Time to Eat Programme.

Each season brings such a wonderful variety of fresh fruits and vegetables. These days, supermarkets stock produce from all over the world and many foods are available all the year round. However, some fruits and vegetables are more abundant when in season in the UK and therefore less expensive. Try to take advantage of these cheaper and delicious seasonal foods and put them to good use with one of the delightful recipes in this book. In June, for example, why not try the Strawberry Syllabub (page 162) or Strawberry Soufflé Omelette (page 180) when there is a wealth of succulent, juicy strawberries available. During the colder months, when apples and pears are at their best, enjoy the Winter Fruit Compote with Port (page 178). In the summer, you can take advantage of tasty vegetables like baby leeks, courgettes, home grown tomatoes and mixed leaves. They work deliciously in salads and as side servings to main meals. Whatever the time of year you'll be sure to find something tasty here!

In the Time to Eat cookbook, you'll find plenty of appetizing recipes to suit your lifestyle, including the various times of the day and week when you eat. There are plenty of mid-week family meals for times when everyone manages to sit down together, but there are also lots of scrumptious snacks for people on the move. And of course, for those special occasions, you'll find some delightful menu plans to suit the mood perfectly. Look up our romantic Valentines Day Menu Plan on page 139 – a delightfully flavoursome, flirtatious meal just for two! There are also many delicious low Point puddings and cakes that will satisfy a sweet tooth at any time of year! Make it your time to start enjoying life to the full. Discover this great way to lose weight successfully while enjoying great food. It's Time to Eat.

soups....
and starters

Main meal minestrone

13 Points per recipe | Takes 15 minutes to prepare, 30 minutes to cook

Serves 4. Calories per serving 275. Freeze ✓

Almost a mini casserole, this delicious soup will warm the cockles of your heart!

225 g (8 oz) extra lean minced beef	**400 g can of chopped tomatoes**
1 teaspoon paprika	**850 ml (1½ pints) beef stock**
175 g (6 oz) carrots, diced	**100 g (3½ oz) soup pasta or quick cook**
1 red pepper, de-seeded and chopped	**macaroni**
1 onion, chopped	**salt and freshly ground black pepper**
1 garlic clove, crushed	**2 tablespoons chopped fresh flat leaf**
225 g (8 oz) courgettes, chopped	**parsley, to serve**

1. Heat a large saucepan, add the mince and dry fry until evenly browned. Stir in the paprika, carrots, red pepper, onion, garlic and courgettes, and cook for 2 minutes.

2. Stir in the tomatoes and stock, and bring to the boil. Reduce the heat, cover and simmer for 15 minutes.

3. Add the pasta and season to taste. Cook for 10 minutes more or until the pasta is tender. Stir in the parsley and serve the soup in four warmed bowls.

try this: *Use turkey or pork mince as an alternative to beef, but remember to change the type of stock you use, too. The Points per serving will be 2½ and 3 respectively.*

Zero Point vegetable broth

0 Points per recipe | **Takes 15 minutes to prepare, 30 minutes to cook**

Ⓥ Ⓥg *if using vegetable stock. Serves 4. Calories per serving 85. Freeze ✓*

Keep a batch of this soup in the fridge and when you're hungry, simply fill up on a bowlful without using any Points.

1 red onion, chopped finely	1 tablespoon tomato purée
225 g (8 oz) carrots, diced	400 g can of chopped tomatoes
3 celery sticks, sliced thinly	salt and freshly ground black pepper
175 g (6 oz) swede, chopped finely	2 tablespoons chopped fresh mixed herbs,
1.2 litres (2 pints) vegetable or chicken	such as chives, parsley, basil and
stock	oregano, to serve

1. Place the onion, carrots, celery, swede, stock, tomato purée and chopped tomatoes in a large saucepan, and bring to the boil.

2. Reduce the heat and simmer gently for 25 minutes, until the vegetables are very tender. Season to taste and stir in the fresh herbs just before serving.

tip: *Take time to chop the vegetables finely to enable some of the vegetables to break down during cooking and thicken the soup. This way you'll have a chunky soup that won't be too watery.*

Spicy thai style sweetcorn soup

3 Points per recipe | **Takes 20 minutes**

Serves 2. Calories per serving 130. Freeze ✗

Thai fish sauce adds a pungent, Oriental flavour to soups and stir fries. It's very salty so add a little, taste the soup and then add more if desired.

600 ml (20 fl oz) vegetable stock	2 tablespoons sherry
1 tablespoon Thai fish sauce	1 teaspoon demerara sugar
1 fresh red chilli, de-seeded and chopped	100 g (3½ oz) canned or frozen sweetcorn
finely	4 spring onions, sliced into long thin strips
1 small garlic clove, chopped finely	1 tablespoon cornflour
finely grated zest of 1 lime	1 tablespoon chopped fresh coriander,
2 tablespoons fresh lime juice	to garnish

1. Place the vegetable stock, fish sauce, chilli, garlic, lime zest, lime juice, sherry and sugar in a large saucepan, and bring to the boil. Reduce the heat and simmer for 5 minutes to allow all the flavours to mingle.

2. Add the sweetcorn and spring onions, and cook until they are heated through.

3. Mix the cornflour with a little cold water to form a paste and add this to the soup, stirring until it thickens. Serve the soup topped with fresh coriander.

try this: *For a more substantial dish add 100 g (3½ oz) canned white crab meat to this flavour-packed soup. The Points will be 2 per serving.*

2 POINTS

Broccoli and stilton soup

8 Points per recipe | Takes 10 minutes to prepare, 25 minutes to cook

V *Serves 4. Calories per serving 155. Freeze ✓*

Stilton has a strong flavour which means you won't need to use as much, so you can save on Points without cutting back on flavour.

450 g (1 lb) broccoli, broken into florets	**1.2 litres (2 pints) vegetable stock**
225 g (8 oz) leeks, sliced	**50 g (1¾ oz) blue Stilton, crumbled**
225 g (8 oz) potatoes, peeled and diced	**salt and freshly ground black pepper**

1. Place the broccoli in a large saucepan with the leeks and potatoes. Add the stock and bring to the boil. Reduce the heat, cover and simmer for 20 minutes.
2. Blend the soup in a food processor or liquidiser in batches, and return the soup to a clean saucepan. Reheat gently.
3. Add the Stilton and heat, stirring, until the cheese dissolves. Season to taste and ladle into four warmed bowls.

try this: *You can use other blue cheeses such as dolcelatte instead of Stilton, but remember to adjust the Points as well.*

1 POINT

Spiced carrot soup

1½ Points per recipe | Takes 10 minutes to prepare, 25 minutes to cook

V **Vg** *Serves 2. Calories per serving 155. Freeze ✓*

Cumin seeds release a strong, pungent flavour when toasted, which means you can add an authentic, spicy taste without adding any extra Points. Serve with 50 g (1¾ oz) of granary bread for 1½ Points per serving.

1 teaspoon cumin seeds	**1 garlic clove, crushed**
350 g (12 oz) carrots, diced	**1 tablespoon tomato purée**
150 g (5½ oz) potatoes, peeled and diced	**600 ml (20 fl oz) vegetable stock**
1 small onion, chopped	**salt and freshly ground black pepper**

1. In a small, heavy based saucepan toast the cumin seeds for 2–3 minutes over a medium heat, until you begin to smell the aroma of the spice. Remove the pan from the heat and set the cumin seeds aside.
2. Place the carrots, potatoes, onion, garlic, tomato purée and stock in a large saucepan, and bring to the boil. Reduce the heat, cover and simmer for 20 minutes.
3. Transfer the cooked soup to a food processor in batches and blend until it is smooth – if you don't have a food processor, push the soup through a sieve.
4. Return the soup to a clean saucepan and add the toasted cumin seeds. Season to taste, stir well and heat through. Ladle the soup into two warmed bowls.

try this: *If you prefer a chunkier soup, then don't blend it, just roughly mash it with a potato masher.*

Curried sweet potato and lentil soup

8 Points per recipe | **Takes 10 minutes to prepare, 35 minutes to cook**

Ⓥ Ⓥg *Serves 4. Calories per serving 170. Freeze ✓*

Sweet potatoes have a wonderful bright orange colour. They are perfect for soups because of their creamy, buttery texture, so you get a sense of richness for so few Points!

450 g (1 lb) sweet potatoes, peeled and diced	850 ml (1½ pints) vegetable stock
1 onion, chopped finely	50 g (1¾ oz) dried split red lentils
1 garlic clove, crushed	salt and freshly ground black pepper
1 tablespoon medium curry powder	2 tablespoons chopped fresh coriander, to garnish

1. Place the sweet potatoes, onion, garlic, curry powder, stock and lentils in a large saucepan and bring to the boil. Reduce the heat, cover and simmer gently for 30 minutes, stirring from time to time.

2. Transfer the soup to a food processor or liquidiser in batches, and blend until smooth.

3. Return the soup to a clean saucepan and heat through. Season to taste, ladle the soup into four warmed bowls and garnish with fresh coriander.

try this: *This soup works very well with parsnips instead of sweet potatoes as they also have a sweet flavour. The Points will be 1½ per serving.*

Courgette and potato soup

1½ Points per recipe | **Takes 15 minutes to prepare, 25 minutes to cook**

Ⓥ Ⓥg *Serves 2. Calories per serving 125. Freeze ✓*

The soy sauce adds the salt to this recipe so you shouldn't need to add any. Check the seasoning before serving and add more soy sauce if necessary.

low fat cooking spray	600 ml (20 fl oz) vegetable stock
1 small onion, chopped finely	2 tablespoons light soy sauce
1 garlic clove, crushed	freshly ground black pepper
150 g (5½ oz) potatoes, peeled and diced	1 tablespoon chopped fresh coriander, to garnish
225 g (8 oz) courgettes, grated coarsely	
1 teaspoon ground coriander	

1. Spray a large saucepan with low fat cooking spray. Place the pan on the heat, and add the onion and garlic. Cook over a medium heat for 5 minutes until the onion has softened, but not browned. Add the potatoes, courgettes and ground coriander, and cook for a further 2–3 minutes.

2. Add the stock and soy sauce, and bring to the boil. Reduce the heat and simmer for 15 minutes, until the potatoes have broken down.

3. Season to taste with freshly ground black pepper and ladle into two warmed soup bowls. Garnish with the fresh coriander and serve.

try this: *To make a creamier soup, stir in 75 g (2¾ oz) low fat soft cheese. This will increase the Points to 2 per serving.*

Creamy vegetable soup

4½ Points per recipe | Takes 15 minutes to prepare, 35 minutes to cook

V Serves 6. Calories per serving 125. Freeze ✓

A steaming mug of hot, creamy vegetable soup is real comfort food. This warming, filling soup is great as a low Point snack, or as a starter if you're feeling really hungry.

225 g (8 oz) carrots, diced	100 g (3½ oz) frozen peas
225 g (8 oz) swede, diced	400 g can of chopped tomatoes
350 g (12 oz) green cabbage, such as	850 ml (1½ pints) vegetable stock
savoy, shredded	300 ml (10 fl oz) skimmed milk
1 onion, chopped	salt and freshly ground black pepper
225 g (8 oz) potatoes, diced	

1. Put the carrots, swede, cabbage, onion, potatoes, peas, chopped tomatoes and stock in a large saucepan. Bring to the boil. Reduce the heat and simmer for 30 minutes.

2. Transfer the soup to a food processor or liquidiser in batches, and blend until smooth. Return it to a clean saucepan, season to taste and then stir in the milk. Heat the soup through and serve.

try this: *If you prefer a chunkier texture, mash the vegetables with a potato masher instead of using a blender.*

Tuna and sweet potato chowder

10½ Points per recipe | Takes 15 minutes to prepare, 15 minutes to cook

Serves 4. Calories per serving 200. Freeze ✗

This hearty soup is a meal in itself; a wonderful filler for a chilly day.

300 ml (10 fl oz) skimmed milk	100 g (3½ oz) canned or frozen sweetcorn
300 ml (10 fl oz) fish stock	200 g (7 oz) canned tuna in brine, drained
1 red onion, chopped finely	and flaked
1 red pepper, de-seeded and chopped finely	1 tablespoon cornflour
2 bay leaves	salt and freshly ground black pepper
350 g (12 oz) sweet potatoes, peeled and	2 tablespoons chopped fresh parsley,
diced finely	to garnish

1. Place the milk, fish stock, onion, red pepper, bay leaves and sweet potatoes in a large saucepan and gently bring to the boil. Reduce the heat and simmer gently for 10 minutes until the potatoes are tender.

2. Stir in the sweetcorn and tuna, and heat through. Season to taste.

3. Mix the cornflour with a little cold water to make a thin paste and add it to the pan. Cook, stirring, until the soup thickens slightly. Serve in four warmed bowls, garnished with chopped parsley.

try this: *Try using canned white crab meat instead of tuna, adding chopped coriander instead of parsley. The Points per serving will remain the same.*

Chunky tomato soup

2½ Points per recipe | **Takes 15 minutes to prepare, 25 minutes to cook**

v *without the Worcestershire sauce. Serves 4. Calories per serving 85. Freeze ✓ (see tip)*
The delicate, peppery taste of the rocket leaves make this tomato soup taste fabulous.

low fat cooking spray	300 ml (10 fl oz) vegetable stock
1 onion, chopped finely	1 tablespoon Worcestershire sauce
2 garlic cloves, crushed	100 ml (3½ fl oz) low fat plain fromage frais
400 g can of chopped tomatoes	salt and freshly ground black pepper
300 ml (10 fl oz) tomato juice	100 g (3½ oz) rocket leaves, to serve

1. Spray a large saucepan with low fat cooking spray, and add the onion and garlic. Cook over a low heat, stirring from time to time, until the onion has softened but not browned, adding a little water if it sticks. This will take about 10 minutes.

2. Add the chopped tomatoes, tomato juice, stock and Worcestershire sauce, and bring to the boil. Reduce the heat, cover and simmer for 15 minutes. Season to taste.

3. Stir in the fromage frais and then ladle the soup into four warmed bowls. Alternatively, you can top the soup with a spoonful of fromage frais (about ½ a tablespoon per serving). Scatter over the rocket leaves, and serve.

tip: *This soup freezes well, but do freeze it before you add the fromage frais. When you are ready to serve, reheat the soup and then continue from step 3.*

Christmas lunch

This delicious Christmas lunch is so low in Points, you'll be able to enjoy other treats too.

Chunky tomato soup *above*, 1 serving.................½ Point
(*pictured left*)

Roast Christmas turkey *page 130*, 1 serving..........5 Points
200 g (7 oz) Boiled potatoes ....2 Points
Zero Point vegetables.....................................0 Points

Christmas pudding *page 185*, 1 serving ....3 Points

Total Points for meal.........................10½ Points

Zero Point celery and leek soup

0 Points per recipe | **Takes 15 minutes to prepare, 25 minutes to cook**

Ⓥ Ⓥg *Serves 4. Calories per serving 50. Freeze ✓*

350 g (12 oz) celery, sliced	850 ml (1½ pints) vegetable stock
350 g (12 oz) leeks, sliced	1 teaspoon caraway seeds
2 garlic cloves, crushed	salt and freshly ground black pepper
2 tablespoons light soy sauce	

1. Place the celery, leeks and garlic in a large saucepan, and stir in the soy sauce. Pour over the vegetable stock, sprinkle in the caraway seeds and bring to the boil. Reduce the heat, season to taste and simmer for 20 minutes.
2. Remove about a third of the soup and set aside. Blend the remainder in a food processor or liquidiser, until smooth.
3. Return the blended and unblended soup to a clean saucepan. Heat through and then serve in warmed bowls.

Creamy cauliflower and broccoli soup

3½ Points per recipe | **Takes 15 minutes to prepare, 25 minutes to cook**

Ⓥ *Serves 4. Calories per serving 120. Freeze ✓*

1 onion, chopped finely	425 ml (15 fl oz) skimmed milk
450 g (1 lb) cauliflower, broken into florets	2 tablespoons cornflour
350 g (12 oz) broccoli, broken into florets	salt and freshly ground black pepper
600 ml (20 fl oz) vegetable stock	

1. Place the chopped onion, cauliflower and broccoli in a large saucepan. Pour in the stock and bring to the boil. Reduce the heat, cover and simmer for 20 minutes.
2. Transfer the soup to a food processor or liquidiser in batches, and blend until smooth. Return the soup to a clean saucepan and add the milk. Cook, stirring, until the soup just comes to the boil.
3. Mix the cornflour with a little cold water to make a paste and stir this into the soup. Cook, stirring, until the liquid thickens a little. Season to taste and serve the soup piping hot.

Leek and potato soup

3½ Points per recipe | **Takes 15 minutes to prepare, 30 minutes to cook**

Ⓥ *Serves 2. Calories per serving 170. Freeze ✓*

1 teaspoon sunflower oil	600 ml (20 fl oz) vegetable stock
225 g (8 oz) leeks, sliced	100 ml (3½ fl oz) skimmed milk
225 g (8 oz) potatoes, peeled and diced	salt and freshly ground black pepper
1 garlic clove, crushed	

1. Heat the oil in a large saucepan, and add the leeks, potatoes and garlic. Cook over a gentle heat for 2–3 minutes, stirring occasionally.
2. Add the stock to the pan and bring to the boil. Reduce the heat, cover and simmer for 25 minutes.
3. Carefully ladle half the soup into a food processor or liquidiser, and blend until smooth. Return the blended soup to the pan, and add the milk and seasoning. Heat through and serve the soup in warmed bowls.

Cannellini bean pâté

12 Points per recipe | **Takes 10 minutes + 2 hours chilling**

v Serves 4. Calories per serving 135. Freeze ✓

This tasty pâté is also delicious as a dip with chunky sticks of carrot, cucumber and celery.

**410 g can of cannellini beans, rinsed and
 drained**

150 g (5½ oz) low fat soft cheese

1 garlic clove, crushed

3 tablespoons low fat mayonnaise

salt and freshly ground black pepper

---

1. Place the cannellini beans in a food processor with the low fat soft cheese, garlic, mayonnaise and seasoning. Blend until smooth.

2. Transfer the pâté to a bowl, cover and chill for 2 hours before serving.

try this: *Canned beans make the perfect base for vegetarian pâtés. Try using butter beans instead of cannellini beans. The Points per serving will remain the same.*

**goes well
with...**

*two water biscuits for
1 extra Point.*

Chinese chicken noodle soup

6½ Points per recipe | **Takes 20 minutes**

Serves 2. Calories per serving 270. Freeze ✗

This soup gives you a taste of the Orient without using too many Points.

---

150 g (5½ oz) cooked chicken

50 g (1¾ oz) fine egg noodles

600 ml (20 fl oz) hot chicken stock

2 tablespoons soy sauce

1 tablespoon tomato ketchup

50 g (1¾ oz) mange tout peas, halved

4 spring onions, sliced into long, thin strips

75 g (2¾ oz) baby sweetcorn, halved

75 g (2¾ oz) fresh beansprouts

1 tablespoon chopped fresh coriander,
   to garnish

---

1. Using two forks shred the chicken meat into thin strands and set aside.

2. Place the noodles in a large saucepan and pour in the hot chicken stock. Stir in the soy sauce and tomato ketchup, and leave it to stand for 5 minutes.

3. Stir the noodles well and place the pan on the hob. Bring to the boil and add the shredded chicken, mange tout peas, spring onions, baby sweetcorn and beansprouts.

4. Simmer the soup for 5 minutes – the vegetables should remain crunchy. Ladle the noodle soup into serving bowls and scatter with fresh coriander.

try this: Ⓥ Ⓥg *For a tasty meat free version, use 225 g (8 oz) diced beancurd instead of the chicken. The Points per person will be 2½.*

Mushroom and garlic soup

3½ Points per recipe | **Takes 15 minutes to prepare, 35 minutes to cook + 20 minutes soaking**

Ⓥ Ⓥg *Serves 2. Calories per serving 155. Freeze ✓*

Dried mushrooms (porcini) are widely available in supermarkets these days; their intense flavour makes them a good addition to soups, stocks and casseroles. They are, of course, Point free!

---

15 g (½ oz) dried mushrooms (porcini)

300 ml (10 fl oz) boiling water

1 tablespoon sunflower oil

100 g (3½ oz) shallots, chopped

1 garlic clove, crushed

125 g (4½ oz) brown cap mushrooms, diced

125 g (4½ oz) shiitake mushrooms, sliced

300 ml (10 fl oz) vegetable stock

1 tablespoon cornflour

salt and freshly ground black pepper

2 tablespoons chopped fresh parsley,
   to serve

---

1. Using a pair of scissors, snip the dried mushrooms into small pieces and place them in a bowl. Pour over the boiling water and leave to stand for 20 minutes. Drain the mushrooms, reserving the liquid.

2. Meanwhile, heat the oil in a large saucepan and add the shallots and garlic. Cook them gently for 5 minutes, until softened. Add the fresh mushrooms, and cook for a further 5 minutes until liquid begins to ooze from them. Add the soaked porcini, the reserved soaking liquid and the stock.

3. Bring the pan to the boil. Reduce the heat, and then cover and simmer for 20 minutes.

4. Transfer the soup to a food processor or liquidiser in batches, and blend until smooth. Return the soup to a clean pan and heat through.

5. Mix the cornflour with a little cold water to make a paste and add this to the soup. Cook, stirring continuously, until the liquid thickens a little. Season to taste, stir in the parsley and ladle the soup into two warmed bowls.

Spicy prawn broth with noodles

7 Points per recipe | Takes 20 minutes

Serves 4. Calories per serving 200. Freeze ✗

850 ml (1½ pints) fish stock	1 red pepper, de-seeded and sliced thinly
2 tablespoons soy sauce	175 g (6 oz) tiger prawns, peeled
2 fresh red chillies, de-seeded and chopped finely	100 g (3½ oz) thin egg noodles
1 garlic clove, chopped	100 g (3½ oz) water chestnuts, sliced
1 teaspoon caster sugar	6 spring onions, sliced
175 g (6 oz) carrots, sliced into matchsticks	2 tablespoons chopped fresh coriander, to garnish

1. Place the stock, soy sauce, chillies, garlic and sugar in a large saucepan and bring to the boil. Add the carrots and pepper, and simmer for 5 minutes.

2. Add the prawns to the soup along with the noodles, water chestnuts and spring onions. Simmer for a further 5 minutes, stirring well to incorporate the noodles.

3. Ladle the soup into four warmed bowls and garnish with the chopped coriander.

Curried aubergine soup

0 Points per recipe | Takes 15 minutes to prepare, 30 minutes to cook

Ⓥ Ⓥg *Serves 4. Calories per serving 80. Freeze ✓*

1 onion, chopped	850 ml (1½ pints) vegetable stock
1 garlic clove, crushed	400 g can of chopped tomatoes
1 tablespoon medium curry powder	salt and freshly ground black pepper
1 aubergine, diced	1 tablespoon chopped fresh coriander, to garnish
225 g (8 oz) carrots, diced	

1. Place the onion, garlic, curry powder, aubergine and carrots in a large saucepan. Add the stock, chopped tomatoes and seasoning. Bring to the boil and then simmer for 25 minutes, until the aubergine is very pulpy.

2. Transfer the soup to a food processor or liquidiser in batches. Blend for a very short time, so the texture of the soup is not entirely smooth. Heat through in a clean saucepan. Garnish with coriander.

Cherry tomato and basil toasts

3½ Points per recipe | Takes 15 minutes

Ⓥ *Serves 2. Calories per serving 130. Freeze ✗*

2 medium slices white bread	1 teaspoon balsamic vinegar
2 teaspoons pesto	1 tablespoon torn fresh basil
150 g (5½ oz) cherry tomatoes, halved	salt and freshly ground black pepper

1. Toast one side of each slice of bread until pale golden.

2. Spread the untoasted side with pesto. Grill for 2–3 minutes. Mix the tomatoes with the vinegar, basil and seasoning. Spoon the mixture over each slice of pesto coated toast and serve.

Garlic mushroom gratin

4 Points per recipe | **Takes 20 minutes**

Ⓥ *Serves 2. Calories per serving 105. Freeze ✗*

This starter will also double up as a quick and easy lunchtime snack.

---

2 teaspoons sunflower oil

225 g (8 oz) button mushrooms, quartered

1 garlic clove, crushed

1 tablespoon soy sauce

2 tablespoons chopped fresh parsley

15 g (½ oz) fresh white breadcrumbs

15 g (½ oz) Parmesan cheese, grated

---

1. Heat the oil in a medium saucepan and add the mushrooms and garlic. Cook over a medium heat for 5 minutes until the mushrooms are softened. Add the soy sauce, and then turn up the heat and allow the pan juices to bubble and evaporate. Add the parsley.

2. Divide the mixture between two individual ramekin dishes. Stir together the breadcrumbs and Parmesan cheese and use the mixture to top each ramekin.

3. Place the ramekin dishes under a medium grill for 3–4 minutes until the topping turns golden. Serve hot.

tip: *Don't throw away any slightly stale bread, use a food processor to make breadcrumbs and keep them in a bag in the freezer. Whenever a recipe requires breadcrumbs you can then take out as much as you like.*

Tuna fish cakes

9½ Points per recipe | **Takes 20 minutes to prepare, 30 minutes to cook + 30 minutes chilling**

Serves 4. Calories per serving 140. Freeze ✓

Make up a batch of these tasty little cakes for a quick snack, or to store in the freezer as a handy standby for those hungry moments. These are delicious served warm with a crisp green salad tossed with shredded spring onions and halved cherry tomatoes.

---

350 g (12 oz) potatoes, peeled and diced

200 g (7 oz) canned tuna in brine, drained
  and flaked

100 g (3½ oz) courgettes, grated

1 tablespoon chopped fresh dill

1 egg, beaten

50 g (1¾ oz) fresh white breadcrumbs

low fat cooking spray

salt and freshly ground black pepper

---

1. Cook the potatoes in a large saucepan of lightly salted, boiling water for 10 minutes, until they are tender. Drain and mash them thoroughly.

2. Add the tuna to the potatoes and mix well. Fold in the courgettes with the dill and seasoning.

3. With your hands, shape the mixture into eight cakes. Put the tuna cakes on a baking sheet lined with non stick baking parchment and place them in the freezer for 30 minutes.

4. Preheat the oven to Gas Mark 5/190°C/fan oven 170°C. Dip the chilled fish cakes into the beaten egg, and then coat them in the breadcrumbs.

5. Spray each tuna cake lightly with low fat cooking spray. Place the cakes on a fresh baking sheet lined with non stick baking parchment. Bake them for 20 minutes until they are golden and crunchy. Serve warm.

tip: *Chilling the cakes before coating them in egg and breadcrumbs makes them easier to handle and ensures they keep their shape well.*

Aubergine and feta rolls

14½ Points per recipe | Takes 10 minutes to prepare, 35 minutes to cook

Ⓥ *Serves 6. Calories per serving 120. Freeze ✗*

Cooking aubergine slices on a griddle pan gives them a delicious roasted flavour and texture, without using up lots of oil.

---

1 aubergine, trimmed at each end

2 tablespoons olive oil

100 g (3½ oz) feta cheese, crumbled

225 g (8 oz) plum tomatoes, chopped finely

1 tablespoon pesto

salt and freshly ground black pepper

1 teaspoon balsamic vinegar, to serve

---

1. Slice the aubergine lengthways into six thin slices, discarding the end slices. Brush each slice with a little olive oil and cook on a griddle pan for 2–3 minutes on each side. Transfer the slices to a plate and set aside.

2. Preheat the oven to Gas Mark 5/190°C/fan oven 170°C. To make the filling, mix together the feta cheese, tomatoes, pesto and seasoning. Place a little of the filling on the top end of each aubergine slice.

3. Roll up each slice, enclosing the filling, and secure the roll with a cocktail stick. Line a baking sheet with non stick baking parchment. Place the aubergine rolls on the baking sheet and bake for 15 minutes.

4. Drizzle each roll with a few drops of balsamic vinegar. Serve the rolls warm, allowing one for each person.

tip: *When buying tomatoes look for a rich, deep red colour and a firm texture as these have the best flavour.*

Cajun potato skins

8 Points per recipe | Takes 20 minutes to prepare + chilling, 1 hour 10 minutes to cook

Ⓥ Ⓥg *Serves 4. Calories per serving 225. Freeze ✗*

This recipe uses a tasty salsa which is also delicious served with grilled chicken or fish.

---

3 x 225 g (8 oz) large baking potatoes

2 teaspoons Cajun spice mix

1 tablespoon sunflower oil

1 teaspoon salt flakes

For the salsa:

225 g (8 oz) mango, diced finely

1 red onion, chopped finely

finely grated zest and juice of 1 lime

1 teaspoon olive oil

225 g (8 oz) plum tomatoes, skinned and
  chopped finely

2 tablespoons chopped fresh coriander

---

1. Preheat the oven to Gas Mark 6/200°C/fan oven 180°C. Prick the potatoes all over and bake them for 50 minutes. Carefully remove them from the oven and slice them in half.

2. Using a small spoon, scoop out the potato flesh from the centre of each half – don't discard the flesh as you can use it for mashed potato at a later date.

3. Cut each potato shell in half. Place the 12 potato skins in a large plastic container with a tight fitting lid and add the Cajun spice, oil and salt flakes. Shake the container well, so each potato skin gets a light coating.

4. Arrange the potato shells on a baking sheet lined with non stick baking parchment. Return them to the oven for 20 minutes, until they are crunchy.

5. To make the salsa, mix together the mango, red onion, lime zest and juice, olive oil, tomatoes and coriander. Chill in the fridge until ready to serve. Serve three crispy Cajun skins per person with a bowl of salsa for dipping.

tip: *To speed things up you can microwave the potatoes, they will take roughly 5 minutes each on High.*

Chicken satay skewers

9½ Points per recipe | **Takes 10 minutes to prepare, 15 minutes to cook + 30 minutes marinating**

Serves 4. Calories per serving 160. Freeze ✓

These are delicious eaten hot or cold, and are ideal for packed lunches or picnics.

350 g (12 oz) skinless chicken breast, chopped into bite sized pieces	1 teaspoon dried chilli flakes
1 garlic clove, crushed	2 tablespoons crunchy peanut butter
2 tablespoons dark soy sauce	1 tablespoon tomato purée
	100 ml (3½ fl oz) pineapple juice

1. Place the chicken in a shallow, non-metallic dish.
2. Mix together the garlic, soy sauce, chilli flakes, peanut butter, tomato purée and pineapple juice. Pour the mixture over the chicken and toss well to coat all the pieces. Cover and leave to marinate for 30 minutes.
3. Thread the chicken pieces on to wooden skewers. Place them under a hot grill for 15 minutes, turning frequently, until evenly browned and cooked through.

tip: *Soak the wooden skewers in water for 20 minutes before using, to prevent them from burning.*

Tuna pâté

9½ Points per recipe | **Takes 5 minutes + 30 minutes chilling**

Serves 4. Calories per serving 115. Freeze ✗

200 g (7 oz) canned tuna in brine, drained	3 tablespoons low fat mayonnaise
125 g (4½ oz) low fat soft cheese	1 teaspoon chopped fresh dill
2 teaspoons freshly squeezed lemon juice	salt and freshly ground black pepper

1. Place the tuna in a bowl and flake the flesh with a fork. Beat in the low fat soft cheese, lemon juice, mayonnaise, dill and seasoning.
2. Spoon the pâté into a small bowl and chill for 30 minutes before serving.

Mini ham and tomato pizzas

4½ Points per recipe | **Takes 10 minutes**

Serves 2. Calories per serving 115. Freeze ✓

1 English muffin, split in half	1 tomato, sliced
1 tablespoon tomato purée	25 g (1 oz) mozzarella light cheese, grated
25 g (1 oz) wafer thin ham	freshly ground black pepper

1. Toast the muffin halves for 1 minute on each side. Spread them with the tomato purée and then top each half with ham and sliced tomato.
2. Sprinkle over a little grated mozzarella cheese and season with black pepper.
3. Return the muffin halves to the grill for 2–3 minutes until the cheese is bubbling. Enjoy them while they are still hot.

tip: *These pizzas are an ideal way to use up slightly stale muffins. Two medium slices of white bread could be used instead if you prefer. The Points will remain the same.*

Chicken satay skewers

Smoked salmon and cucumber twists

3 Points per recipe | Takes 20 minutes

Serves 1. Calories per serving 140. Freeze ✗

100 g (3½ oz) cucumber	½ teaspoon horseradish sauce
50 g (1¾ oz) smoked salmon	1 tablespoon low fat plain fromage frais
1 tablespoon low fat mayonnaise	freshly ground black pepper

1. Slice both the cucumber and salmon into six long, thin strips. Twist one strip of salmon around each cucumber stick.
2. Mix together the mayonnaise, horseradish sauce and fromage frais, and drizzle over the salmon and cucumber twists. Season with a light grinding of black pepper.

Smoked salmon mousse

2½ Points per recipe | Takes 25 minutes + 30 minutes chilling

Serves 2. Calories per serving 80. Freeze ✗

Try serving this with shop bought melba toasts; three toasts per serving will increase the Points to 1½.

50 g (1¾ oz) smoked salmon	1 small egg white
100 g (3½ oz) low fat plain cottage cheese	salt and freshly ground black pepper
finely grated zest of ½ lime	

1. Using small kitchen scissors, snip the salmon into tiny pieces and set aside.
2. Place the cottage cheese in a sieve and allow it to drain for 10 minutes.
3. Discard the liquid and then push the cottage cheese through the sieve, using the back of a spoon.
4. Beat the smoked salmon pieces, lime zest and seasoning into the cottage cheese.
5. Whisk the egg white until it forms stiff peaks. Using a metal spoon, fold it into the smoked salmon mixture – don't over stir or you will knock out the air from the mousse.
6. Spoon the mousse into two individual ramekin dishes and chill for 30 minutes.

Garlic prawn cocktail

5½ Points per recipe | Takes 15 minutes

Serves 2. Calories per serving 150. Freeze ✗

175 g (6 oz) raw tiger prawns, peeled	2 tablespoons half fat crème fraîche
1 teaspoon olive oil	100 g (3½ oz) Iceberg or Little Gem lettuce,
1 garlic clove, sliced thinly	shredded
1 tablespoon chopped fresh flat leaf parsley	a pinch of cayenne pepper
1 teaspoon tomato purée	

1. Rinse the prawns and pat them dry with kitchen paper. Heat the oil in a frying pan and add the garlic, prawns and parsley. Cook, stirring, for 2–3 minutes, until the prawns turn pink.
2. Add the tomato purée and crème fraîche to the pan, and stir well.
3. Divide the shredded lettuce between two plates or shallow bowls, and spoon the prawn mixture between them. Sprinkle with a little cayenne pepper and serve at once.

Spring rolls

11½ Points per recipe | **Takes 20 minutes to prepare, 15 minutes to cook**

Serves 4. Calories per serving 265. Freeze ✗

These tasty, crunchy vegetable and prawn rolls have all the flavour of those served in Chinese restaurants, but they are only a fraction of the Points since they are baked and not deep fried.

---

low fat cooking spray

100 g (3½ oz) carrots, sliced into thin strips

100 g (3½ oz) white cabbage, shredded

1 small red pepper, de-seeded and sliced
   thinly

100 g (3½ oz) fresh prawns, peeled

100 g (3½ oz) fresh beansprouts

2 tablespoons dark soy sauce, plus extra
   for dipping

¼ teaspoon Chinese five spice powder

8 sheets filo pastry

2 tablespoons sunflower oil

---

1. To make the filling, spray a large frying pan with low fat cooking spray. Add the carrots, cabbage, red pepper, prawns, beansprouts, soy sauce and five spice powder. Stir fry for 2 minutes. Remove the pan from the heat and allow the mixture to cool a little.

2. Preheat the oven to Gas Mark 5/190°C/fan oven 170°C. Line a baking sheet with non stick baking parchment.

3. Brush a sheet of filo pastry with a little of the oil. Spoon some of the filling on to one end of the pastry sheet. Roll the pastry up, tucking in the edges to enclose the filling so that you end up with a sausage shape. Repeat this process with the remaining pastry sheets until you have eight spring rolls.

4. Place the spring rolls on the baking sheet and bake for 10 minutes until they are golden and crispy. Serve them hot with extra soy sauce for dipping, allowing two spring rolls per person.

**goes well
with...**

*sweet chilli sauce.
2 tablespoons is
½ a Point.*

Moules marinières

5½ Points per recipe | Takes 20 minutes

Serves 2. Calories per serving 200. Freeze ✗

Juicy, plump mussels gently steamed in garlic, wine and parsley are wonderful. Remember to serve them with a finger bowl as it can be a messy job eating them!

---

2 shallots, sliced

2 garlic cloves, crushed

100 ml (3½ fl oz) dry white wine

4 tablespoons chopped fresh parsley

1 kg (2 lb 4 oz) mussels, washed and
   scrubbed

freshly ground black pepper

---

1. Place the shallots, garlic, wine and 100 ml (3½ fl oz) water in a large saucepan. Add the parsley and mussels. Season with lots of freshly ground black pepper.

2. Cover the pan and bring to the boil. Turn down the heat slightly and cook, covered, for 5 minutes, until all the mussel shells have opened. Discard any that have not opened. Ladle into warmed bowls and serve immediately.

tip: *When preparing mussels, discard any open ones that don't snap shut when gently tapped. Any mussels that have not opened after they have been cooked should also be thrown away.*

try this: *Use a crusty piece of French bread to soak up the delicious juices from the mussels, wine and garlic, remembering to add the extra Points.*

Curried chicken dippers

9 Points per recipe | Takes 20 minutes + chilling + 20 minutes marinating

Serves 4. Calories per serving 145. Freeze ✓ (dippers only)

These tasty nuggets are ideal for buffets.

For the dippers:

100 ml (3½ fl oz) low fat plain yogurt

1 tablespoon medium curry powder

2 garlic cloves, crushed

½ teaspoon ground turmeric

2 tablespoons freshly squeezed lemon juice

2 tablespoons chopped fresh coriander

½ teaspoon salt

350 g (12 oz) skinless, boneless chicken
   breasts, cut into long, thin strips

For the dip:

150 ml (5 fl oz) low fat plain yogurt

1 tablespoon mint jelly

100 g (3½ oz) cucumber, diced finely

---

1. Mix together the yogurt, curry powder, garlic, turmeric, lemon juice, coriander and salt. Spoon this mixture over the chicken and stir to coat all the strips well.

2. Cover and leave the chicken to marinate for 20 minutes.

3. Meanwhile, prepare the dip. Beat together the yogurt, mint jelly and cucumber. Chill in the fridge until required.

4. Place the chicken under the grill and cook the pieces under a medium heat for 10 minutes, turning frequently, until the chicken is cooked through.

5. Serve the dippers hot or cold with the dip alongside.

Ricotta and pesto mushrooms

12 Points per recipe | Takes 35 minutes

Ⓥ *Serves 4. Calories per serving 170. Freeze ✗*

450 g (1 lb) open cup (large) mushrooms (12 of similar size)	low fat cooking spray
175 g (6 oz) baby spinach leaves	175 g (6 oz) ricotta cheese
a pinch of ground nutmeg	2 tablespoons pesto
	salt and freshly ground black pepper

1. Preheat the oven to Gas Mark 5/190°C/fan oven 170°C. Line a baking sheet with non stick baking parchment.
2. Remove the stalks from the mushrooms and chop them finely. Place the chopped stalks in a medium saucepan with the spinach, nutmeg and 2 tablespoons of water. Cover and cook for 2 minutes until the spinach wilts. Remove the pan from the heat, drain well and allow the mixture to cool a little.
3. Place the mushrooms, cup side down, on the baking sheet and spray each one with low fat cooking spray. Bake them for 10 minutes.
4. Remove the mushrooms from the oven and drain away any liquid. Turn the mushrooms cup side up.
5. Mix the cooled spinach mixture with the ricotta cheese, pesto and seasoning. Spoon this mixture into the mushroom cups. Return the mushrooms to the oven for 10 minutes and then serve them hot, allowing three per person.

Stuffed tomatoes

9 Points per recipe | Takes 15 minutes to prepare, 20 minutes to cook

Ⓥ *Serves 4. Calories per serving 130. Freeze ✗*

Zero Point tomatoes make great containers for a tasty stuffing – and they look so attractive, too.

4 beefsteak tomatoes	1 garlic clove, crushed
200 g (7 oz) baby spinach leaves	50 g (1¾ oz) fresh wholemeal breadcrumbs
2 teaspoons sunflower oil	50 g (1¾ oz) Parmesan cheese, shaved
1 small onion, chopped	salt and freshly ground black pepper
225 g (8 oz) mushrooms, diced	

1. Slice the tops off the tomatoes and, using a small spoon, carefully scoop out the centre seeds, taking care not to break through the skin. Place the tomatoes, cut side down, on a double layer of kitchen paper and let them drain.
2. Preheat the oven to Gas Mark 6/200°C/fan oven 180°C. Place the spinach in a medium saucepan with 2 tablespoons of water. Cover and cook over a low heat for 2–3 minutes until the spinach wilts. Drain thoroughly.
3. Heat the oil in a frying pan. Add the onion, mushrooms and garlic. Then stir fry them gently for 5 minutes, until they are softened. Add the wilted spinach and mix well. Remove the pan from the heat and stir in the breadcrumbs, Parmesan cheese and seasoning.
4. Place the tomato shells in a roasting tin, cut side up, and fill them with the spinach and cheese mixture. Bake for 20 minutes until you see that the tomatoes are beginning to soften. Don't overcook them or they may collapse.

salads…

and light bites

3 POINTS

Hot peppered chicken and spinach salad

5½ Points per recipe | Takes 15 minutes to prepare, 20 minutes to cook

Serves 2. Calories per serving 200. Freeze ✗

The contrasting colours of the red skinned apples and the deep green spinach make this a very attractive and appetising dish.

---

2 x 125 g (4½ oz) skinless chicken breasts	**1 tablespoon fresh lemon juice**
1 tablespoon freshly ground mixed pepper	**175 g (6 oz) baby spinach leaves**
low fat cooking spray	**3 tablespoons low fat plain yogurt**
1 red skinned dessert apple (e.g. Braeburn)	**1 tablespoon finely chopped fresh chives**

---

1. Preheat the oven to Gas Mark 6/200°C/fan oven 180°C. Line a baking sheet with non stick baking parchment.

2. Season the chicken breasts generously with the mixed pepper and spray them lightly with low fat cooking spray. Place the chicken on the prepared baking sheet and roast it for 20 minutes.

3. Core the apple and slice it thinly. Toss it together with the lemon juice and baby spinach leaves and divide the mixture between two plates.

4. Mix the yogurt with the chives. Slice each chicken breast on the slant – each breast should give 5–6 slices. Pile the slices randomly on top of the spinach and apple. Drizzle with the yogurt and chive dressing, and serve.

tip: *Add the chicken while it is still warm, this way it begins to just wilt the spinach.*

Summer salad

4½ Points per recipe | Takes 10 minutes

V *Serves 2. Calories per serving 200. Freeze ✗*

Crunchy green vegetables are delicious tossed in this creamy, tangy orange dressing.

For the salad:

225 g (8 oz) leeks, sliced into rings

225 g (8 oz) sugar snap peas

225 g (8 oz) asparagus spears, trimmed

300 ml (10 fl oz) hot vegetable stock

salt and freshly ground black pepper

For the dressing:

3 tablespoons low fat mayonnaise

3 tablespoons low fat plain yogurt

grated zest of 1 orange

2 tablespoons fresh orange juice

1. Place the leeks, sugar snap peas and asparagus in a medium saucepan with the stock, and bring to the boil. Simmer for 2 minutes, drain and leave to cool.

2. Arrange the vegetables on a serving dish and season.

3. To make the dressing, mix together the mayonnaise, yogurt, orange zest and juice. Drizzle the dressing over the vegetables and serve.

tip: *When trimming asparagus, hold the spear at the top and bottom and then bend it. It will snap in the natural place where the stalk is tough. Discard the tough part.*

Zero Point carrot salad

0 Points per recipe | Takes 10 minutes

V **Vg** *Serves 4. Calories per serving 35. Freeze ✗*

This is a great zero Point side salad that goes with just about anything.

175 g (6 oz) bulb of fennel, shredded

225 g (8 oz) carrots, grated coarsely

100 g (3½ oz) radishes, sliced thinly

4 tablespoons fat free vinaigrette

1 tablespoon finely chopped fresh chives,
     to garnish

1. Place the fennel, carrots, radishes and vinaigrette in a large bowl, and mix together thoroughly.

2. Pile the salad into a serving dish and scatter with the chives.

tip: *This salad will last for up to two days if kept in an airtight container in the fridge.*

Caesar salad

9 Points per recipe | Takes 15 minutes to prepare, 20 minutes to cook

Serves 2. Calories per serving 260. Freeze ✗

Bags of prepared salad are readily available in supermarkets these days. The great advantage of these is you get lots of different salad leaves without the expense of buying a variety of whole lettuces.

1 thick slice of white bread, cubed	200 g bag of mixed lettuce leaves
low fat cooking spray	25 g (1 oz) Parmesan cheese, shaved
2 eggs	3 tablespoons low fat Caesar style dressing
25 g (1 oz) canned anchovy fillets, drained to remove excess oil	freshly ground black pepper

1. Preheat the oven to Gas Mark 4/180°C/fan oven 160°C. Arrange the bread cubes on a baking sheet. Spray them lightly with low fat cooking spray and bake them for 12–15 minutes until they are golden and crunchy croûtons.
2. Meanwhile, cook the eggs in boiling water for 8 minutes, until they are hard boiled. When they are cooked, run them under cold water to prevent a black ring forming around the yolk. When cooled, peel off the shells and cut the eggs into quarters.
3. Pat the anchovies with kitchen paper to absorb any excess oil. Chop them into small pieces and mix them together with the mixed leaves and Parmesan cheese shavings in a salad bowl.
4. Top the salad with the egg quarters and crunchy croûtons. Drizzle the dressing over the top and season with freshly ground black pepper.

tips: *Use a potato peeler to make shavings from Parmesan cheese.*
Most of the top supermarkets sell delicious low fat Caesar dressings which are only 1 Point for 3 tablespoons.

Oriental prawn salad

5½ Points per recipe | Takes 15 minutes

Serves 2. Calories per serving 360. Freeze ✗

Succulent prawns mingled with the juicy, sweet flesh of ripe mango make a perfect combination.

150 g (5½ oz) fine green beans, halved	For the dressing:
350 g (12 oz) ripe mango	zest and juice of 1 lime
150 g (5½ oz) fresh beansprouts	1 tablespoon clear honey
4 spring onions, sliced	1 tablespoon Thai fish sauce
300 g (10½ oz) cooked tiger prawns, peeled	2 tablespoons chopped fresh coriander
150 g (5½ oz) Chinese leaves, shredded	

1. In a small saucepan, cook the beans for 2–3 minutes in lightly salted, boiling water. Drain and refresh them under cold running water.
2. Peel the mango and dice the flesh roughly. Toss the mango together with the cooked beans, beansprouts, spring onions, prawns and Chinese leaves.
3. Mix together the dressing ingredients and drizzle this over the salad. Toss everything together well and pile the salad into a serving bowl.

try this: *Although tiger prawns look attractive in this dish, you can use ordinary peeled prawns as a cheaper alternative.*

Italian pasta salad

17½ Points per recipe | Takes 20 minutes + chilling

V *Vg* *Serves 4. Calories per serving 315. Freeze ✗*

The home made pesto in this recipe is every bit as tasty as the shop bought version, but it is much lower in Points.

225 g (8 oz) pasta twists	1 garlic clove, crushed
75 g (2¾ oz) stoned black olives	2 tablespoons fresh lemon juice
25 g (1 oz) pine nut kernels	225 g (8 oz) cherry tomatoes, halved
15 g (½ oz) fresh basil leaves	salt and freshly ground black pepper
1 tablespoon olive oil	

1. Cook the pasta according to the packet instructions. This should take about 10 minutes. Drain well.
2. To make the pesto, place the olives, pine kernels, basil leaves, olive oil, garlic, lemon juice and seasoning in a food processor. Blend until all the ingredients are chopped evenly and you have a coarse paste. If you don't have a food processor, you can use a pestle and mortar.
3. Toss the pesto into the cooked pasta along with the cherry tomatoes. Cover and chill until required.

tip: *Toss the pesto with the pasta while it is still warm. The pasta will absorb the flavours better.*

Potato salad

12 Points per recipe | Takes 15 minutes + chilling

V *Serves 4. Calories per serving 140. Freeze ✗*

Mixing low fat mayonnaise with low fat fromage frais makes a low Point dressing with a delicious tang.

450 g (1 lb) baby new potatoes, halved	4 tablespoons low fat mayonnaise
6 spring onions, sliced	4 tablespoons low fat plain fromage frais
100 g (3½ oz) gherkins, chopped finely	salt and freshly ground black pepper

1. Cook the potatoes in a large saucepan of lightly salted, boiling water until tender. This will take about 10 minutes. Drain them and allow to cool.
2. Toss the cooled potatoes with the spring onions, gherkins, mayonnaise, fromage frais and seasoning. Cover and chill the salad before serving.

try this: *Add the zest of 1 orange to the salad to give it an extra zing, without adding any extra Points.*

Zero Point coleslaw

0 Points per recipe | Takes 15 minutes + chilling

V *Vg* *Serves 4. Calories per serving 60. Freeze ✗*

A great with everything coleslaw that will bulk out any meal, and all for zero Points!

1 red onion, sliced thinly	225 g (8 oz) carrots, grated coarsely
350 g (12 oz) white cabbage, shredded finely	1 tablespoon finely chopped fresh chives
200 g (7 oz) red cabbage, shredded finely	5 tablespoons fat free vinaigrette dressing

1. Toss together the onion, cabbages, carrots, chives and dressing in a bowl. Cover and chill in the refrigerator.

try this: *Add other zero Point vegetables such as beansprouts or diced red and green pepper.*

Moroccan couscous salad

4 POINTS

15½ Points per recipe | **Takes 15 minutes + 10 minutes standing + chilling**

Ⓥ Ⓥᵍ *Serves 4. Calories per serving 295. Freeze ✗*

This delicious salad can be stir fried for a few minutes and then served as a hot dish!

275 g (9½ oz) couscous	zest of 1 lemon
a pinch of ground cinnamon	2 tablespoons fresh lemon juice
300 ml (10 fl oz) boiling vegetable stock	3 tablespoons chopped fresh mint
50 g (1¾ oz) ready to eat dried apricots	salt and freshly ground black pepper
225 g (8 oz) cucumber, chopped finely	
175 g (6 oz) tomatoes, de-seeded and chopped finely	

1. Place the couscous in a bowl with the cinnamon. Pour over the boiling stock, mix well and cover the bowl with clingfilm. Leave to stand for 10 minutes.

2. Using scissors, snip the apricots into small pieces.

3. Fluff up the couscous with a fork – by this time all the grains should be plump and separate from each other. Add the apricots, cucumber, tomatoes, lemon zest, lemon juice, mint and seasoning. Cover the salad and chill until required.

tip: *The flavour of this salad actually improves if you leave it overnight in the fridge.*

Mixed bean and smoked mackerel salad

6½ POINTS

25½ Points per recipe | **Takes 20 minutes + 1 hour chilling**

Serves 4. Calories per serving 385. Freeze ✗

Smoked mackerel has a strong, salty flavour that really complements the pasta and beans in this salad. This oily fish contains Omega 3 fatty acids which also makes it very good for you.

100 g (3½ oz) small pasta shapes	225 g (8 oz) smoked mackerel fillet, skinned
1 green pepper, de-seeded and chopped finely	2 tablespoons chopped fresh flat leaf parsley
1 red pepper, de-seeded and chopped finely	juice of 1 lemon
1 red onion, chopped finely	salt and freshly ground black pepper
425 g (15 oz) canned mixed beans, rinsed and drained	

1. Cook the pasta according to the packet instructions. Drain well and refresh it under cold water. Mix the pasta together with the peppers, red onion and mixed beans.

2. Remove any bones from the mackerel fillet and flake the flesh. Add it to the pasta mixture with the parsley, lemon juice and seasoning.

3. Cover and chill in the refrigerator for an hour before serving.

try this: *If you want a more subtle flavour, try using smoked trout fillets instead of smoked mackerel. The Points will be reduced to 4 per serving.*

Glazed turkey salad

7½ Points per recipe | Takes 15 minutes to prepare, 15 minutes to cook

Serves 4. Calories per serving 190. Freeze ✗

350 g (12 oz) turkey escalopes

2 tablespoons dark soy sauce

1 tablespoon tomato purée

1 garlic clove, crushed

2 teaspoons clear honey

2 teaspoons sunflower oil

150 g (5½ oz) mange tout peas, halved
   lengthways

150 g (5½ oz) carrots, cut into matchsticks

100 g (3½ oz) canned water chestnuts,
   drained and sliced

100 g (3½ oz) mushrooms, sliced

6 spring onions, sliced very finely

1 head of Chinese leaves, shredded

1. Cut the turkey into thin strips and mix it with the soy sauce, tomato purée, garlic and honey.

2. Heat the sunflower oil in a large frying pan or wok. Stir fry the turkey for 8–10 minutes until cooked through and a glaze starts to form a sticky coating around the strips.

3. Add the mange tout peas, carrots, water chestnuts and mushrooms, and cook for a further 2 minutes.

4. Remove the pan from the heat and toss in the spring onions and shredded Chinese leaves. Divide between four plates and serve at once.

try this: **V** *For a vegetarian alternative, use cubes of firm tofu instead of turkey. Tofu is great at absorbing flavours so it works well with this tangy glaze. The Points per serving will be 1½.*

tip: *Turkey absorbs other flavours very well. If time permits, allow the turkey to marinate for 20 minutes so the flavours really have time to develop.*

Crispy potato and parmesan salad

8½ Points per recipe | Takes 25 minutes

Serves 4. Calories per serving 125. Freeze ✗

Turkey rashers taste every bit as good as bacon, but are lower in Points – perfect for this delicious salad.

350 g (12 oz) baby new potatoes, halved

125 g (4½ oz) turkey rashers

25 g (1 oz) Parmesan shavings

100 g (3½ oz) watercress, washed

150 g (5½ oz) lambs lettuce, washed

salt and freshly ground black pepper

1. Cook the potatoes in a large saucepan of lightly salted, boiling water, until tender. This should take about 10 minutes. Drain them well.

2. Meanwhile, grill the turkey rashers until crispy. Drain them on kitchen paper and chop them into small pieces.

3. Toss the cooked potatoes, turkey rashers and Parmesan shavings together, and season.

4. Pile the watercress and lambs lettuce in a salad bowl and top with the potato mixture.

Goat's cheese salad

22½ Points per recipe | **Takes 25 minutes**

V *Serves 4. Calories per serving 300. Freeze ✗*
Melted cheese on toast makes this a very special salad.

150 g (5½ oz) French stick, cut into 2.5 cm
   (1 inch) slices
low fat cooking spray
150 g (5½ oz) goat's cheese, sliced thinly
225 g (8 oz) fine green beans
2 Little Gem lettuces, shredded

150 g (5½ oz) baby spinach leaves
salt and freshly ground black pepper
For the dressing:
1 teaspoon white wine vinegar
1 teaspoon caster sugar
1 teaspoon sesame oil

1. Preheat the oven to Gas Mark 5/190°C/fan oven 170°C. Spray each slice of French stick with a little low fat cooking spray and bake in the oven for 5 minutes until crunchy.
2. Top the bread with the goat's cheese slices and return to the oven for 5 minutes, until the cheese begins to melt.
3. Meanwhile, cook the beans in lightly salted, boiling water for 2 minutes. Drain and refresh them under cold running water. Toss them together with the lettuce and spinach.
4. Mix together the dressing ingredients and drizzle this over the salad. Toss everything thoroughly and then divide the salad between four plates. Top the salad with the goat's cheese toasts and a generous grinding of black pepper.

try this: *If you want to add a little colour to the salad, add 225 g (8 oz) halved cherry tomatoes or a thinly sliced, de-seeded red pepper. The Points will remain the same.*

goes well with...

cranberry sauce. 1 tablespoon is ½ a Point.

Breakfast salad

16½ Points per recipe | Takes 15 minutes to prepare, 15 minutes to cook

Serves 4. Calories per serving 185. Freeze ✗

This substantial salad is perfect for a lunchtime treat or brunch to stave off those hunger pangs.

225 g (8 oz) low fat sausages	1 tablespoon wholegrain mustard
150 g (5½ oz) lean back bacon	1 tablespoon dark soy sauce
low fat cooking spray	1 teaspoon clear honey
225 g (8 oz) open cup mushrooms, sliced	350 g (12 oz) Iceberg lettuce, shredded
225 g (8 oz) cherry tomatoes, halved	

1. Grill the sausages for about 10 minutes until evenly browned and cooked through, and grill the bacon until crispy. Slice the sausages into rings and chop the bacon into small pieces.

2. Meanwhile, spray a frying pan with the low fat cooking spray and add the mushrooms. Cook them for 5 minutes until they are tender. Add the tomatoes, mustard, soy sauce and honey, and cook for a further 2 minutes, stirring occasionally. Add the sausages and bacon, and mix everything well.

3. Divide the Iceberg lettuce between four serving plates and top with the 'breakfast' mix. Serve at once.

try this: **(V)** *For a vegetarian alternative, omit the bacon and use vegetarian sausages instead. The Points will be 2 per serving.*

Grilled halloumi and tomato platter

4½ Points per recipe | Takes 15 minutes

(V) *Serves 1. Calories per serving 200. Freeze ✗*

Halloumi cheese originates from Cyprus; it has a dense, chewy texture that softens up beautifully when cooked.

low fat cooking spray	1 tablespoon torn fresh basil leaves
50 g (1¾ oz) Halloumi cheese, sliced thinly	1 teaspoon balsamic vinegar
1 beefsteak tomato, sliced	¼ teaspoon sugar
50 g (1¾ oz) cucumber, sliced thickly	salt and freshly ground black pepper

1. Spray a small frying pan with low fat cooking spray and add the Halloumi cheese slices. Cook them for 2–3 minutes on each side until golden.

2. On a large, flat platter, arrange the cooked cheese with the tomato slices and cucumber in alternating layers. Scatter over the fresh basil.

3. Mix together the balsamic vinegar and sugar, and drizzle it over the salad. Season the salad with a little salt and a generous grinding of black pepper, and serve.

tip: *Use a griddle pan to cook the cheese, if you have one, this way you will get attractive markings across each slice.*

Roasted tomato pizzas

5½ Points per recipe | Takes 15 minutes to prepare, 1 hour to cook

V *Serves 2. Calories per serving 170. Freeze ✗*

Oven roasting tomatoes really intensifies their flavour which makes these pizzas particularly satisfying.

350 g (12 oz) plum tomatoes

1 teaspoon salt

1 tablespoon balsamic vinegar

1 tablespoon torn fresh basil

1 English muffin, split

low fat cooking spray

2 teaspoons tomato purée

50 g (1¾ oz) half fat Cheddar, grated

freshly ground black pepper

1. Preheat the oven to Gas Mark 3/160°C/fan oven 140°C. Cut the tomatoes in half and place them, cut side up, on a grill rack resting on a baking sheet. Scatter them with the salt and freshly ground black pepper and bake them for 1 hour – you are really just drying out the tomatoes rather than cooking them.
2. Transfer the roasted tomatoes to a bowl and mix them with balsamic vinegar and basil.
3. Spray each muffin half with low fat cooking spray and grill for 2–3 minutes until they are crunchy and golden.
4. Spread each muffin half with 1 teaspoon of tomato purée, and top with roasted tomatoes and grated cheese. Return them to the grill for 2–3 minutes, until the cheese melts.

tip: *Choose well ripened tomatoes for the best results. While the oven is on, cook up a large batch of oven-roasted tomatoes and then keep them in the refrigerator for salads and sandwiches.*

Cheesy mustard puddings

10½ Points per recipe | Takes 10 minutes to prepare, 15 minutes to cook + 5 minutes standing

V *Serves 4. Calories per serving 130. Freeze ✗*

Made in individual ramekin dishes, these cheesy little pots make an excellent starter or light snack. Serve them hot with a crisp zero Point green salad tossed with a little zero Point vinaigrette.

75 g (2¾ oz) fresh white breadcrumbs

2 eggs, beaten

2 teaspoons wholegrain mustard

200 ml (7 fl oz) skimmed milk

75 g (2¾ oz) half fat Red Leicester cheese, grated

salt and freshly ground black pepper

1. Preheat the oven to Gas Mark 5/190°C/fan oven 170°C.
2. Mix together the breadcrumbs, beaten eggs, mustard, milk, cheese and seasoning. Divide the mixture between four ramekin dishes. Leave to stand for 5 minutes.
3. Bake the dishes in the oven for 15 minutes. The puddings will rise slightly like a soufflé, so you need to serve them at once.

tip: *Try and use crumbs made from bread that is a couple of days old, they soak up the moisture better.*

try this: *The Red Leicester cheese gives these puddings a rich colour, but use Cheddar cheese if you prefer its flavour.*

Noodles in a pot

2½ Points per recipe | **Takes 20 minutes**

Ⓥ *Serves 1. Calories per serving 210. Freeze* ✗

This is a do it yourself pot noodle! It's far more nutritious and tastes great.

25 g (1 oz) fine egg noodles	25 g (1 oz) frozen peas
300 ml (10 fl oz) vegetable stock	1 tablespoon tomato purée
25 g (1 oz) frozen vegetarian mince, defrosted	1 tablespoon dark soy sauce
50 g (1¾ oz) carrots, diced finely	2 spring onions, sliced thinly
	1 teaspoon cornflour

1. Place the noodles in a small saucepan with the stock. Bring to the boil and then add the vegetarian mince, carrots, peas, tomato purée and soy sauce.

2. Simmer gently for 5 minutes and then add the spring onions.

3. Mix the cornflour with a little cold water to make a thin paste and stir this into the pan. Cook, stirring, until the liquid thickens a little. Simmer for 1 minute and then ladle into a soup bowl or mug.

try this: *You can use extra lean beef mince if you prefer. You will need to dry fry it before adding the other ingredients. Use beef stock instead of vegetable stock. Alter the Points to 3 per serving.*

Cheese and red pepper pâté

5½ Points per recipe | **Takes 20 minutes to prepare, 20 minutes to cook + 2 hours chilling**

Ⓥ *Serves 4. Calories per serving 110. Freeze* ✗

Serve this pâté with chunky sticks of carrots, celery or cucumber as a tasty low Point snack – perfect to take to the office for lunch!

low fat cooking spray	50 g (1¾ oz) dried, split red lentils
2 red peppers, de-seeded and chopped finely	300 ml (10 fl oz) vegetable stock
1 red onion, chopped	50 g (1¾ oz) half fat Red Leicester cheese, grated
1 garlic clove, crushed	salt and freshly ground black pepper

1. Heat a medium size saucepan and spray it with the low fat cooking spray. Add the red peppers, onion, garlic and 3 tablespoons of water. Cover and cook over a gentle heat for 5 minutes or until the vegetables begin to soften.

2. Stir in the lentils and stock. Bring to the boil and simmer uncovered for 20 minutes, stirring until the lentils turn mushy and the liquid evaporates.

3. Add the grated cheese and seasoning, and beat the mixture well. Spoon the pâté into four individual ramekin dishes. Chill for at least 2 hours before serving.

try this: *For a smoother pâté, purée the vegetable and lentil mixture in a food processor before beating in the cheese.*

Kidney bean and roasted pepper wraps

13 Points per recipe | **Takes 10 minutes to prepare, 20 minutes to cook**

V **Vg** *Serves 4. Calories per serving 215. Freeze ✗*

These delightful, spicy wraps make a tasty alternative to sandwiches. Make up the filling beforehand, allowing it to cool before filling each tortilla wrap.

1 red pepper, de-seeded and diced	**1 tablespoon sweet chilli sauce**
1 green pepper, de-seeded and diced	**finely grated zest of 1 lime**
2 garlic cloves, crushed	**2 tablespoons chopped fresh coriander**
low fat cooking spray	**4 flour tortillas, heated according to packet**
300 g (10½ oz) canned red kidney beans,	**instructions**
rinsed and drained	**salt and freshly ground black pepper**

1. Preheat the oven to Gas Mark 6/200°C/fan oven 180°C. Line a roasting tin with foil. Place the peppers in the tin and then mix in the garlic. Spray with low fat cooking spray, season and then roast them for 15 minutes.

2. Remove the tin from the oven and add the red kidney beans, sweet chilli sauce and lime zest. Return to the oven for a further 5 minutes.

3. Sprinkle the coriander over the mixture. Spoon the filling equally between the tortillas. Roll them up. Slice the tortillas diagonally in half and arrange them on a serving plate.

try this: *If you like, top the filling of each tortilla with a tablespoon of half fat crème fraîche. This will add 1½ Points per serving.*

Crab omelette rolls

8½ Points per recipe | **Takes 20 minutes**

Serves 2. Calories per serving 275. Freeze ✗

Serve these delicious omelette rolls with fresh green salad leaves, such as watercress mixed with shredded Iceberg lettuce.

3 eggs	**100 g (3½ oz) canned white crab meat,**
1 tablespoon finely chopped fresh chives	**drained**
1 tablespoon soy sauce	**100 g (3½ oz) low fat soft cheese**
1 teaspoon sunflower oil	**a small bunch of watercress, chopped**
	salt and freshly ground black pepper

1. Beat together the eggs, chives, soy sauce, seasoning and 3 tablespoons of water. Heat the oil in a 23 cm (9 inch) frying pan and add the egg mixture.

2. Cover the pan and cook gently for 5 minutes until the egg mixture has set. Scatter over the crab meat, and then dot with the soft cheese. Finally sprinkle the watercress on top.

3. Remove the pan from the heat and gently slide the omelette on to a chopping board or clean surface.

4. Roll up the omelette, enclosing the filling. Slice the roll into eight rings and serve, allowing four rings per person.

tip: *Invest in a good heavy based non stick frying pan, it really is the key to making successful omelettes.*

try this: *Try using flaked, canned tuna in brine instead of crab meat. The Points will be 4½ per serving.*

Croque monsieur

4½ Points per recipe | Takes 15 minutes

Serves 1. Calories per serving 265. Freeze ✗

This is the classic French toasted sandwich, but it's much lower in Points than the original version!

---

2 thin slices of white bread

25 g (1 oz) low fat soft cheese

25 g (1 oz) wafer thin ham

25 g (1 oz) half fat Cheddar cheese, grated

freshly ground black pepper

---

1. Spread 1 slice of bread with half of the low fat soft cheese and top with the ham.
2. Place the remaining slice of bread on top. Grill both sides of the sandwich until pale golden.
3. Mix together the remaining low fat soft cheese and the grated Cheddar cheese and spread this over one side of the grilled sandwich. Season with freshly ground black pepper and return the sandwich to the grill for 2–3 minutes until the cheese melts and starts to brown. Serve at once.

try this: *Add slices of tomato to the sandwich filling before toasting. The Points will remain the same.*

Spicy bean pot

10 Points per recipe | Takes 15 minutes

ⓥ **ⓥg** *Serves 2. Calories per serving 350. Freeze ✗*

Baked beans are always a good standby to have as a speedy snack. Liven them up a little with this tasty idea.

---

420 g can of baked beans

2 shallots, chopped

2 tablespoons tomato purée

1 teaspoon curry powder

15 g (½ oz) sultanas

2 medium pitta breads

1. Place the beans in a medium size saucepan with the shallots, tomato purée, curry powder and sultanas. Heat through gently and simmer for 2–3 minutes.
2. Lightly toast the pitta breads in the oven or in a toaster and cut each one into thin slices.
3. Divide the bean mixture between two small bowls and serve the pitta bread slices alongside to mop up the juices.

try this: *To add extra bite, add a pinch of chilli powder. You can also stuff the bean mixture inside the pitta bread, if you prefer.*

Pasta lunch pot

9½ Points per recipe | **Takes 25 minutes**

V *Serves 2. Calories per serving 355. Freeze* ✗

When you're bored of sandwiches for lunch, pack up a portion of this filling pasta dish and take it to work.

125 g (4½ oz) pasta shapes such as shells
   or bows
low fat cooking spray
1 red pepper, de-seeded and diced
100 g (3½ oz) courgettes, diced
4 spring onions, sliced
2 celery sticks, sliced thinly

110 g (4 oz) button mushrooms, halved
50 g (1¾ oz) canned sweetcorn, drained
2 tablespoons low fat mayonnaise
2 tablespoons 0% fat Greek style plain yogurt
1 teaspoon finely grated lemon zest
salt and freshly ground black pepper

1. Bring a large saucepan of lightly salted water to the boil and add the pasta. Cook for 8–10 minutes until tender, drain well and refresh under cold running water. Set aside.

2. Meanwhile, spray a large non stick frying pan with low fat cooking spray and add the pepper, courgettes, spring onions, celery and mushrooms. Cook, covered, for 5 minutes, and then remove the pan from the heat and add the sweetcorn.

3. Mix together the mayonnaise, yogurt, lemon zest and seasoning, and fold this into the pasta. Add the vegetables and mix well. Spoon the pasta mix into a container with a tight fitting lid and chill until required.

Mushroom sloppy joes

10½ Points per recipe | **Takes 10 minutes to prepare, 15 minutes to cook**

V *Serves 4. Calories per serving 130. Freeze* ✗

Sloppy Joes are a popular American dish which are normally made with mince. This mushroom version is simply delicious!

350 g (12 oz) large button mushrooms,
   quartered
2 garlic cloves, crushed
low fat cooking spray
150 ml (5 fl oz) vegetable stock
290 g can of 99% fat free condensed
   mushroom soup

2 tablespoons half fat crème fraîche
4 medium slices of wholemeal bread
salt and freshly ground black pepper
1 tablespoon chopped fresh parsley,
   to garnish

1. Place the mushrooms and garlic in a pan, spray with low fat cooking spray and cook them gently for 5 minutes.

2. Add the stock and seasoning, and cook over a high heat for 5 minutes. Stir in the soup and heat through.

3. Add the crème fraîche and stir well. Remove from the heat. Toast the bread.

4. Top the four slices of toast with the mixture. Scatter over the parsley and serve.

try this: *There is such a wide variety of mushrooms available in supermarkets. Try experimenting with different types such as oyster, shiitake or brown cap mushrooms.*

Crispy potato cakes

8½ Points per recipe | Takes 25 minutes + 10 minutes cooling

Serves 4. Calories per serving 165. Freeze ✗

This makes an excellent brunch when you want something a little bit different. If you like, dish up each serving of potato cakes (2 cakes) with a poached egg on top. This will add 1½ Points per serving.

225 g (8 oz) carrots	**1 tablespoon chopped fresh parsley**
450 g (1 lb) floury potatoes, peeled but left whole	**low fat cooking spray**
	150 g (5½ oz) turkey rashers
1 egg, beaten	**salt and freshly ground black pepper**

1. Simmer the carrots and potatoes in lightly salted, boiling water for 5 minutes. Drain and let them cool for about 10 minutes, and then grate them coarsely.

2. Mix the grated carrot and potato with the egg, parsley and seasoning.

3. Heat a heavy frying pan until very hot and spray it with a little low fat cooking spray. Place eight large tablespoons of the mixture in the pan, leaving a little space between each one. Flatten them a little with the back of a spoon. You may need to do all this in two batches.

4. Cook over a low heat for 5 minutes on each side, until the potato cakes are golden and cooked through.

5. Meanwhile, grill the turkey rashers until crispy. Serve two cakes per person topped with the crispy rashers.

tip: *It's quite important to use a floury potato such as Desirée for this recipe – waxy ones will not give the same results.*

Cheesy hammy muffins

8½ Points per recipe | Takes 20 minutes

Serves 2. Calories per serving 260. Freeze ✗

This is a delicious brunch dish for those special mid mornings when you have a little time on your hands.

150 g (5½ oz) baby spinach leaves	**1 teaspoon malt vinegar**
1 English muffin, split in half	**2 large eggs**
30 g (1¼ oz) wafer thin ham	**salt and freshly ground black pepper**
2 reduced fat cheese slices	

1. Place the spinach in a small saucepan with 2 tablespoons of water and a little seasoning. Cover and heat gently for 2 minutes until the spinach wilts.

2. Meanwhile, lightly toast the muffin halves and top each with wafer thin ham and a slice of cheese – keep them warm while poaching the eggs.

3. Bring a large saucepan of water to the boil and add the vinegar. With the handle of a wooden spoon, swirl the water and, as you do so, crack in an egg – the swirling of the water helps the egg white stay together. Gently simmer for 2–3 minutes, depending on how soft you like the yolk. Using a slotted spoon, remove the egg from the water and drain it on a double layer of kitchen paper. Repeat the process with the other egg.

4. Squeeze any excess moisture out of the spinach and spoon it on the cheese and ham topped muffins. Finally place a poached egg on each one. Season with black pepper and serve immediately.

Chicken tikka lunch box

18 Points per recipe | **Takes 35 minutes + marinating**

Serves 4. Calories per serving 340. Freeze ✗

You can pack this into a small, plastic container and take it to work for a delicious lunch.

225 g (8 oz) skinless chicken breast, diced

100 g (3½ oz) low fat plain yogurt

1 tablespoon Tikka curry powder

1 tablespoon fresh lemon juice

1 garlic clove, crushed

225 g (8 oz) basmati rice

2 teaspoons sunflower oil

1 red pepper, de-seeded and chopped

1 green pepper, de-seeded and chopped

1 fresh green chilli, de-seeded and chopped finely

1 red onion, chopped

15 g (½ oz) sultanas

salt

1. Mix the chicken with the yogurt, Tikka curry powder, lemon juice and garlic. Leave to marinate for 20 minutes.

2. Meanwhile, cook the basmati rice in lightly salted, boiling water for about 12 minutes, following the packet instructions.

3. Heat the oil in a large saucepan, add the chicken and its marinade and stir fry for 10 minutes, until the chicken is cooked through. Add the peppers, chilli and onion, and cook for a further 5 minutes.

4. Mix the cooked rice and sultanas into the pan, and heat through. Serve hot. Alternatively, allow it to cool and then chill in the fridge to serve as a salad.

try this: *Use chicken thigh meat instead of chicken breast, if you prefer. The Points will be 6 per serving.*

Working lunch

This satisfying lunch will help to keep you on track at work and it's a great reward for a morning of hard work!

Chicken tikka lunch box *above*, 1 serving ....4½ Points *(pictured left)*

Sticky carrot and ginger slice *page 197*, 1 slice.........3 Points

Total Points per meal..........................**7½ Points**

Tuna and sweetcorn open sandwich

7½ Points per recipe | Takes 10 minutes

Serves 2. Calories per serving 220. Freeze ✗

125 g (4½ oz) canned tuna in brine, drained	1 tomato, sliced
25 g (1 oz) canned sweetcorn, drained	75 g (2¾ oz) Iceberg lettuce, shredded
3 tablespoons low fat mayonnaise	2 medium slices of brown bread
50 g (1¾ oz) cucumber, chopped finely	salt and freshly ground black pepper

1. Mix together the tuna with the sweetcorn, low fat mayonnaise and cucumber.
2. Divide the sliced tomato and shredded Iceberg lettuce between the two slices of bread, and then top with the tuna mixture. Season to taste. Slice in half to serve two.

try this: *You can, of course, use canned salmon instead of tuna but it will increase the Points to 4 ½ per serving.*

Chinese style scrambled eggs

5½ Points per recipe | Takes 15 minutes

Serves 2. Calories per serving 215. Freeze ✗

1 teaspoon sunflower oil	3 tablespoons skimmed milk
4 spring onions, sliced	1 tablespoon light soy sauce
100 g (3½ oz) fresh beansprouts	50 g (1¾ oz) cooked prawns, peeled
3 eggs	

1. Heat the sunflower oil in a small saucepan and add the spring onions and beansprouts. Stir fry for 2 minutes until they begin to soften.
2. Beat together the eggs, milk and soy sauce, and add the mixture to the pan with the prawns. Cook, stirring continuously, until the eggs begin to scramble. This will take about 5 minutes. Serve immediately.

try this: *Serve this tasty snack on toast; a medium slice will add 1 Point per serving.*

Chilli chips

10 Points per recipe | Takes 10 minutes to prepare, 20 minutes to cook

Ⓥ Ⓥg *Serves 4. Calories per serving 175. Freeze ✗*

700 g (1 lb 9 oz) potatoes, scrubbed and cut into thick wedges	1 teaspoon chilli flakes
	1 teaspoon Marmite
1 tablespoon olive oil	2 tablespoons boiling water
1 teaspoon paprika	1 tablespoon finely chopped fresh chives

1. Preheat the oven to Gas Mark 6/200°C/fan oven 180°C.
2. Rinse the potato wedges and pat dry with kitchen paper. Place them in a bowl.
3. Mix together the oil, paprika, chilli flakes, Marmite and boiling water. Drizzle this mixture over the potatoes and toss them well to make sure they are evenly coated.
4. Line a baking tray with non stick baking parchment. Arrange the potato wedges on the tray and bake them for 20 minutes or until crispy and cooked through. Scatter with chives and serve hot.

pasta...

rice, noodles & pulses

Pad thai

17 Points per recipe | Takes 20 minutes + 10 minutes standing

Serves 4. Calories per serving 330. Freeze ✓

Pad Thai is a traditional noodle dish from Thailand with a fresh, spicy, piquant flavour that makes it an excellent dish.

225 g (8 oz) thin egg noodles	**225 g (8 oz) carrots, grated or cut into**
2 tablespoons Thai fish sauce	**thin strips**
2 tablespoons tomato purée	**150 g (5½ oz) fresh beansprouts**
1 teaspoon caster sugar	**6 spring onions, cut into long, thin strips**
1 teaspoon rice wine vinegar	**175 g (6 oz) prawns, peeled**
low fat cooking spray	To serve:
150 g (5½ oz) white cabbage, shredded	**25 g (1 oz) salted peanuts, chopped**
	1 teaspoon chilli flakes

1. Place the noodles in a large bowl and pour boiling water over to just cover them. Leave them to stand for 10 minutes. Mix together the fish sauce, tomato purée, sugar and rice wine vinegar. Set aside.

2. Drain the noodles thoroughly. Spray a large non stick frying pan or wok with low fat cooking spray, and add the noodles, cabbage, carrots, beansprouts and spring onions. Stir fry for 5 minutes.

3. Add the prawns and fish sauce mixture to the pan, and stir fry for 2–3 minutes until it is all piping hot.

4. Transfer to four warmed serving dishes, and scatter with the chopped peanuts and chilli flakes.

Rice and vegetable lunch pot

12½ Points per recipe | Takes 25 minutes to prepare, 45 minutes to cook

V **Vg** *Serves 4. Calories per serving 290. Freeze ✓*

This tasty mixture of brown rice and vegetables is equally delicious eaten hot or cold. Pack it in a plastic container for a filling and tasty lunchtime snack.

225 g (8 oz) brown rice	**150 g (5½ oz) mushrooms, sliced**
225 g (8 oz) carrots, diced	**2 tablespoons dark soy sauce**
1 onion, chopped	**700 ml (1¼ pints) vegetable stock**
1 green pepper, de-seeded and diced	**2 tablespoons tomato purée**
1 red pepper, de-seeded and diced	**100 g (3½ oz) frozen peas**

1. Place the rice in a large saucepan with the carrots, onion, peppers and mushrooms. Mix together the soy sauce, stock and tomato purée, and then add this mixture to the rice and vegetables.

2. Bring everything to the boil. Reduce the heat, cover and simmer gently for 35 minutes, stirring from time to time.

3. Stir in the frozen peas. Cover and cook for a further 5–10 minutes, until all the liquid has been absorbed and the rice is tender. Serve warm, or chill in the fridge and serve as a rice salad.

try this: *Try adding a tablespoon of curry powder to the rice while it is cooking, to add a hint of spice. The Points will remain the same.*

Tuna and wild rice bake

22 Points per recipe | Takes 25 minutes to prepare, 20 minutes to cook

Serves 4. Calories per serving 350. Freeze ✓

Low fat condensed soup makes an excellent and easy sauce. It adds a rich flavour to this tasty tuna bake.

225 g (8 oz) mixed long grain white and wild rice	**185 g can of tuna in brine, drained and flaked**
low fat cooking spray	**300 ml (10 fl oz) skimmed milk**
150 g (5½ oz) button mushrooms, sliced	**1 teaspoon chopped fresh dill or ½ teaspoon dried dill**
225 g (8 oz) leeks, sliced	**50 g (1¾ oz) half fat Cheddar cheese, grated**
4 celery sticks, sliced	**salt and freshly ground black pepper**
350 g can of 99% fat free condensed mushroom soup	

1. Cook the white and wild rice as directed on the packet and drain thoroughly.

2. Meanwhile, heat a large saucepan and spray it with low fat cooking spray. Add the mushrooms, leeks and celery, and cook them over a medium to low heat, stirring, until the vegetables have softened.

3. Mix in the mushroom soup, tuna, skimmed milk, dill and seasoning. Add the cooked rice and stir well.

4. Preheat the oven to Gas Mark 5/190°C/fan oven 170°C.

5. Spoon the rice mixture into an ovenproof dish and top with the grated cheese. Bake for 20 minutes until the cheese is melted and bubbling. Serve hot.

tip: *You can buy the long grain white rice and wild rice already mixed together.*

Smoked haddock kedgeree

22½ Points per recipe | **Takes 45 minutes**

Serves 4. Calories per serving 415. Freeze ✓

Kedgeree was originally served at breakfast time, but it's so tasty it is also great as a simple lunch or supper dish.

2 eggs	350 g (12 oz) smoked haddock, skinned and
2 teaspoons sunflower oil	cubed
250 g (9 oz) long grain white rice	100 g (3½ oz) frozen peas
1 onion, chopped	3 tablespoons 0% fat Greek style plain
1 tablespoon medium curry powder	yogurt
700 ml (1¼ pints) fish stock	2 tablespoons chopped fresh parsley
	salt and freshly ground black pepper

1. Boil the eggs in a small saucepan of boiling water, this will take 10 minutes. Drain the eggs and peel them.

2. Heat the oil in a large saucepan, and add the rice, onion and curry powder. Stir to make sure the rice grains are evenly coated with the curry powder and oil, and cook for 1 minute.

3. Add the stock and bring to the boil. Simmer for 10 minutes, by which time at least half of the stock will be absorbed.

4. Add the haddock and peas, and cook for a further 6–8 minutes; take care not to stir too much, or the fish will break up.

5. Fold in the yogurt and season to taste. Sprinkle over the chopped parsley. Cut the hard boiled eggs into quarters, arrange them over the top, and serve.

tip: *After hard boiling eggs, run them under cold water for a good 2–3 minutes, this will prevent a black ring forming around the yolk.*

Butternut squash risotto

20 Points per recipe | **Takes 40 minutes**

Ⓥ *Serves 4. Calories per serving 400. Freeze ✓*

The secret of making a good risotto is to add the liquid a little at a time, and wait for it to be absorbed before adding more.

1 tablespoon olive oil	850 ml (1½ pints) boiling vegetable stock
1 onion, chopped	100 g (3½ oz) low fat garlic and herb soft
300 g (10½ oz) risotto rice	cheese
450 g (1 lb) butternut squash, peeled and	2 tablespoons torn fresh basil
cubed	salt and freshly ground black pepper

1. Heat the olive oil in a large saucepan, and add the onion and rice. Cook, stirring for 2 minutes, and then add the butternut squash.

2. Gradually add the stock a little at a time and cook, stirring almost continuously, until the rice has absorbed the liquid, and is creamy and tender. This will take about 20 minutes.

3. Stir in the soft cheese, basil and seasoning. Serve the risotto in four warmed shallow bowls.

try this: *Butternut squash has rich, orange-coloured flesh. If you have difficulty finding one, use pumpkin or marrow instead; they will taste just as good. The Points will remain the same.*

Moroccan spiced rice with lamb

26½ Points per recipe | **Takes 30 minutes to prepare, 20 minutes to cook**

Serves 4. Calories per serving 430. Freeze ✗

With the authentic combination of ginger, cinnamon and mint, this Moroccan dish is absolutely delicious.

350 g (12 oz) lean lamb mince	**225 g (8 oz) courgettes, diced**
1 onion, sliced	**225 g (8 oz) long grain white rice**
2 garlic cloves, crushed	**400 ml (14 fl oz) lamb stock**
½ teaspoon ground ginger	**450 g (1 lb) plum tomatoes, skinned,**
½ teaspoon ground cinnamon	**de-seeded and diced**
1 teaspoon paprika	**2 tablespoons chopped fresh mint, plus a**
1 aubergine, diced	**few extra leaves, to garnish**

1. Heat a heavy based non stick frying pan and add the lamb mince. Dry fry for 5 minutes, draining off any excess fat. Add the onion, garlic, ginger, cinnamon and paprika, and stir well.

2. Add the aubergine, courgettes, rice and stock, and bring to the boil. Cover and simmer for 20 minutes until the stock has been absorbed and the rice is tender.

3. Add the tomatoes and mint, and heat through. Spoon the mixture into a warmed serving dish and scatter with a few extra mint leaves.

tip: *The easiest way to skin tomatoes is to plunge them into boiling water for a few seconds – the skins will then peel off easily.*

Thai style rice

12½ Points per recipe | **Takes 5 minutes to prepare, 15 minutes to cook**

Ⓥ Ⓥ**g** *Serves 2. Calories per serving 395. Freeze ✓*

The texture of Thai rice is a lot stickier than ordinary long grain rice, so don't worry if the cooked grains are not separate and fluffy! This is delicious with any of the Thai curries, such as the beef curry on page 147.

175 g (6 oz) jasmine (Thai) rice	**100 g (3½ oz) canned pineapple, drained**
100 ml (3½ fl oz) 88% fat free coconut milk	**and chopped finely**
½ teaspoon salt	**2 tablespoons chopped fresh coriander**
1 fresh red chilli, de-seeded and chopped	
finely	

1. Place the rice, coconut milk, salt, chilli and 300 ml (10 fl oz) water in a large saucepan. Stir well and bring to the boil.

2. Reduce the heat, cover the pan and simmer for 10–12 minutes until the rice is tender – stir the rice from time to time to prevent it sticking to the bottom of the pan.

3. Add the pineapple and fresh coriander. Serve at once.

tip: *Keep a careful eye on the pan while cooking as anything with milk in it has a tendency to boil over. Keep the heat as low as you can.*

Special egg fried rice

18 Points per recipe | Takes 35 minutes

Serves 4. Calories per serving 365. Freeze ✓

Egg fried rice no longer needs to be a weekend treat. This simple version is much lower in Points than a portion from a Chinese takeaway, but just as delicious.

low fat cooking spray	½ teaspoon Chinese five spice powder
1 onion, chopped	600 ml (20 fl oz) vegetable or chicken stock
150 g (5½ oz) carrots, chopped finely	100 g (3½ oz) lean ham, diced
1 red pepper, de-seeded and chopped finely	100 g (3½ oz) cooked prawns, peeled
225 g (8 oz) long grain white rice	150 g (5½ oz) fresh beansprouts
2 tablespoons soy sauce	2 eggs

1. Heat a large saucepan and spray it with low fat cooking spray. Add the onion, carrots and pepper and stir fry for 2 minutes. Stir in the rice, soy sauce, five spice powder and stock, and bring to the boil. Reduce the heat, cover and simmer for 10 minutes.

2. Remove the cover, turn up the heat and add the ham, prawns and beansprouts.

3. Beat the eggs with 3 tablespoons of water. Push the rice to one side of the pan and spray some more low fat cooking spray in the cleared space. Pour the eggs into the cleared space and cook until they set.

4. Break up the cooked egg with a spatula and incorporate it into the rice mixture. Spoon into four serving bowls and serve with extra soy sauce, if you like.

try this: *Use leftover chicken instead of the ham if you like. Simply shred the meat with two forks and add it to the rice in step 2. The Points will remain the same.*

Salmon risotto cakes

13 Points per recipe | Takes 40 minutes

Serves 4. Calories per serving 250. Freeze ✓

Using rice rather than the usual mashed potato in these fish cakes adds a unique and tasty twist to a traditional recipe.

200 g (7 oz) risotto rice	100 g (3½ oz) canned red salmon, drained and flaked
225g (8 oz) mushrooms, chopped finely	1 tablespoon chopped fresh tarragon
1 garlic clove, chopped	low fat cooking spray
3 shallots, chopped finely	salt and freshly ground black pepper
700 ml (1¼ pints) vegetable stock	

1. Place the rice, mushrooms, garlic, shallots and 150 ml (5 fl oz) of the stock in a large saucepan and cook gently, stirring until the stock has been absorbed. Gradually add the remaining stock and cook until all the stock has been absorbed and the rice is tender. This will take 20 minutes.

2. Allow the rice mixture to cool, and then mix in the flaked salmon, seasoning and tarragon. Shape the mixture into eight cakes with your hands.

3. Heat a heavy based frying pan and spray it with low fat cooking spray. Cook the risotto cakes for 3–4 minutes on each side until golden. Serve them warm, allowing two cakes per person.

try this: *Try using canned tuna in brine instead of the salmon. The Points per serving will remain the same.*

Indian style pilaff

9 Points per recipe | **Takes 20 minutes to prepare, 15 minutes to cook**

V **Vg** *Serves 2. Calories per serving 395. Freeze ✓*

This colourful mix of vegetables with a hint of spice is a perfect accompaniment to grilled meat, fish or chicken.

1 teaspoon sunflower oil	½ teaspoon chilli powder
1 small onion, chopped	½ teaspoon cumin seeds
1 garlic clove, chopped	½ teaspoon ground coriander
125 g (4½ oz) carrots, diced	600 ml (20 fl oz) vegetable stock
1 red pepper, de-seeded and diced	50 g (1¾ oz) frozen peas
150 g (5½ oz) basmati rice	2 tablespoons chopped fresh coriander
1 teaspoon ground turmeric	

1. Heat the oil in a large saucepan and add the onion, garlic, carrots, pepper, rice, turmeric, chilli powder, cumin seeds and ground coriander. Stir well and cook for 2 minutes.

2. Add the stock and cook, covered, for 15 minutes until virtually all the stock has been absorbed and the rice is just tender. Add the peas and cook for a further 2–3 minutes.

3. Sprinkle over the fresh coriander and serve.

try this: *Add 225 g (8 oz) cooked shredded chicken for a more substantial dish. The Points will be 7 per serving.*

Spicy jambalaya

22½ Points per recipe | **Takes 30 minutes to prepare, 20 minutes to cook**

Serves 4. Calories per serving 435. Freeze ✓

For a taste of the Caribbean, try this hot and spicy Jambalaya.

low fat cooking spray	1 green pepper, de-seeded and diced
50 g (1¾ oz) chorizo, diced finely	3 celery sticks, sliced
1 onion, chopped	225 g (8 oz) long grain white rice
2 garlic cloves, chopped	600 ml (20 fl oz) chicken stock
350 g (12 oz) turkey breasts, sliced thinly	125 g (4½ oz) canned red kidney beans, drained and rinsed
1 teaspoon cayenne pepper	100 g (3½ oz) canned pineapple chunks in natural juice, drained
½ teaspoon ground ginger	
1 fresh green chilli, de-seeded and chopped finely	2 tablespoons chopped fresh coriander
1 red pepper, de-seeded and diced	

1. Heat a large frying pan and spray it with low fat cooking spray. Add the chorizo, onion, garlic, turkey strips, cayenne pepper, ginger and chopped chilli. Stir fry for 5 minutes until the turkey changes colour.

2. Add the peppers, celery, rice and stock and bring to the boil. Cover and cook for 20 minutes, stirring occasionally, until the rice is tender and the stock has been absorbed.

3. Add the kidney beans, pineapple and coriander. Heat through and serve at once.

Red lentil and aubergine curry

11 Points per recipe | **Takes 25 minutes to prepare, 30 minutes to cook**

V **Vg** *Serves 4. Calories per serving 210. Freeze* ✓

The lentils, aubergine and coconut combine beautifully to make a lovely rich sauce.

---

low fat cooking spray

1 onion, chopped

2 garlic cloves, crushed

2 tablespoons medium curry powder

½ teaspoon salt

1 aubergine, diced

175 g (6 oz) dried, split red lentils

600 ml (20 fl oz) vegetable stock

100 ml (3½ fl oz) 88% fat free coconut milk

2 tablespoons chopped fresh coriander

---

1. Spray a frying pan with low fat cooking spray and gently cook the onion and garlic until softened, but not browned. Stir in the curry powder and cook for 1 minute.

2. Add the salt, aubergine, lentils and stock to the pan. Bring to the boil and simmer uncovered for 30 minutes, stirring regularly to prevent the lentils sticking.

3. By this time the lentils should be tender and mushy – if not raise the heat and boil vigorously for 5 minutes. Add the coconut milk and coriander, and mix well. Heat through and serve.

try this: *If you want to reduce the Points for this curry, leave out the coconut milk and stir in 2 tablespoons of tomato purée instead. You will save 1 Point per serving.*

goes well with...

half a medium naan bread per serving for an extra 4 Points.

Chicken and mushroom risotto

10½ Points per recipe | Takes 45 minutes

Serves 2. Calories per serving 395. Freeze ✓

1 teaspoon olive oil	150 g (5½ oz) mushrooms, sliced
125 g (4½ oz) skinless chicken breast, sliced into thin strips	150 g (5½ oz) risotto rice
	600 ml (20 fl oz) chicken stock
2 shallots, chopped finely	1 teaspoon chopped fresh tarragon
1 garlic clove, crushed	salt and freshly ground black pepper

1. Heat the olive oil in a large frying pan, and stir fry the chicken for 2–3 minutes to seal it on all sides. Add the shallots, garlic and mushrooms to the pan and cook for a further 2 minutes.

2. Add the rice, and then stir in a little stock. Once this has been absorbed, stir in a little more. Keep doing this until all the stock is used up, this will take about 20 minutes.

3. Add the chopped tarragon and season to taste. Serve at once.

tips: *Risotto is really at its best as soon as it is made; if it is left and reheated, it becomes stodgy. Ideally it should have a creamy almost sloppy consistency – if you prefer it a little drier, just cook the rice for a few more minutes.*

You can use cooked, leftover chicken for this recipe, too. You won't need to stir fry it first though.

Polenta with garlic mushrooms

20½ Points per recipe | Takes 40 minutes + 30 minutes setting

V *Serves 4. Calories per serving 355. Freeze ✗*

Polenta makes an interesting alternative to rice and pasta.

2 vegetable stock cubes, crumbled	450 g (1 lb) open cup mushrooms, halved
350 g (12 oz) polenta	2 garlic cloves, chopped finely
2 tablespoons finely chopped fresh chives	salt and freshly ground black pepper
25 g (1 oz) Parmesan cheese, grated	1 tablespoon chopped fresh parsley,
low fat cooking spray	to garnish

1. In a large saucepan, bring 850 ml (1½ pints) water and the crumbled stock cubes to a fast boil. Add the polenta and beat well. Reduce the heat and simmer for 5 minutes, stirring continuously.

2. Remove the pan from the heat and beat in the chives and Parmesan cheese. Pour the polenta mixture into a 18 cm x 23 cm (7 inch x 9 inch) shallow non stick square tin and allow it to set in the fridge for about 30 minutes.

3. When the polenta is firm to the touch, turn it out on to a clean board or work surface. Cut it into eight triangles and spray the pieces with low fat cooking spray. Cook them on a griddle pan for 2–3 minutes each side until they are warmed through and light brown.

4. Meanwhile, spray a frying pan with low fat cooking spray, and add the mushrooms and garlic. Season and cook them for 5 minutes, stirring frequently until the mushrooms are tender.

5. To serve, arrange two triangles of polenta on each serving plate and top with the garlic mushrooms. Garnish with a little chopped parsley.

tips: *If you don't own a griddle pan, just grill the polenta triangles under a hot grill for 2–3 minutes each side. It is important to keep stirring the pan as you cook the polenta to prevent lumps from forming.*

You can make polenta up to two days before you need it, keep it well covered in the fridge and griddle portions of it whenever you want.

Sun dried tomato couscous

12 Points per recipe | **Takes 25 minutes + 15 minutes standing**

V **Vg** *Serves 2. Calories per serving 430. Freeze ✓*

Couscous is so quick and easy to prepare yet it provides such a filling, attractive and tasty meal.

175 g (6 oz) couscous	25 g (1 oz) stoned black olives, quartered
175 ml (6 fl oz) boiling water	4 spring onions, sliced
½ vegetable stock cube	1 tablespoon sesame seeds
25 g (1 oz) sun dried tomatoes, chopped	salt and freshly ground black pepper
finely	2 tablespoons torn fresh basil leaves,
1 tablespoon sun dried tomato purée	to garnish

1. Place the couscous in a bowl and pour over the boiling water. Crumble in the stock cube and stir in the sun dried tomatoes and tomato purée. Cover the bowl with clingfilm and leave it to stand for 15 minutes. The couscous will absorb the water and become tender.

2. Add the olives and spring onions to the couscous.

3. Gently dry fry the sesame seeds in a small saucepan until they begin to brown. Add them to the couscous. Season, garnish with the basil leaves, and serve.

tip: *This dish will improve if you leave it a while to let the flavours mingle. If time permits, make it the day before and keep it in the fridge until required.*

Moroccan couscous with minted chicken

26½ Points per recipe | **Takes 30 minutes + 30 minutes marinating**

Serves 4. Calories per serving 470. Freeze ✓

A simple yet stunning dish that will go down well at any dinner party.

4 x 125 g (4½ oz) skinless chicken breasts	275 g (9½ oz) couscous
2 garlic cloves, chopped	350 ml (12 fl oz) boiling vegetable stock
2 tablespoons chopped fresh mint	100 g (3½ oz) ready to eat dried apricots,
finely grated zest and juice of 1 lemon	chopped finely
¼ teaspoon ground cinnamon	2 tablespoons chopped fresh flat leaf parsley
1 teaspoon caster sugar	150 g (5½ oz) courgettes, grated coarsely
2 teaspoons olive oil	salt and freshly ground black pepper

1. Make vertical slits along the top of each chicken breast. Place them in a shallow non metallic dish.

2. Mix together the garlic, mint, lemon zest and juice, cinnamon, caster sugar and oil. Drizzle this mixture over the chicken. Cover and leave to marinate for at least 30 minutes.

3. Meanwhile, place the couscous in a bowl and pour over the hot stock. Fluff up the grains with a fork and cover with clingfilm. Leave to stand for 15–20 minutes until the grains have absorbed the liquid and are plump. Mix in the chopped apricots, parsley, grated courgettes and seasoning.

4. Grill the chicken breasts for 6–8 minutes each side until cooked through.

5. To serve, spoon a mound of couscous on to each serving plate and top with a grilled chicken breast.

tip: *The longer you leave the chicken to marinate the better the flavour, so if you have time, refrigerate it overnight.*

try this: *Add de-seeded, diced red and green peppers to the couscous for added colour but no more Points.*

Butter bean and leek stroganoff

11 Points per recipe | Takes 30 minutes

V Serves 2. Calories per serving 310. Freeze ✗

This stroganoff is delicious served with a medium jacket potato or 200 g (7 oz) of freshly cooked pasta. Each suggestion adds an extra 2½ Points per serving.

low fat cooking spray

225 g (8 oz) leeks, sliced

150 g (5½ oz) mushrooms, sliced

1 garlic clove, crushed

1 teaspoon paprika

150 ml (5 fl oz) vegetable stock

420 g can of butter beans, drained and
   rinsed

100 ml (3½ fl oz) half fat crème fraîche

1 tablespoon cornflour

2 tablespoons sherry

salt and freshly ground black pepper

2 tablespoons chopped fresh parsley,
   to serve

1. Spray a large saucepan with low fat cooking spray and add the leeks, mushrooms and garlic. Cook, stirring, for 5 minutes until the vegetables have softened. Stir in the paprika and cook for 1 minute.

2. Add the stock and bring to the boil. Cover and simmer for 5 minutes, and then stir in the butter beans and crème fraîche.

3. Mix the cornflour with the sherry to form a paste, and add it to the pan. Cook, stirring, until the sauce thickens.

4. Season to taste and scatter with the chopped parsley to serve.

tip: *Always mix the cornflour to a paste with a cold liquid, hot liquid will thicken it as soon as you add it.*

Spicy italian pasta

3½ Points per recipe | Takes 25 minutes

V Serves 1. Calories per serving 325. Freeze ✗

When you want something simple for lunch, but a sandwich just doesn't fit the bill, try this tasty pasta for one – delicious eaten hot or cold.

60 g (2 oz) pasta shells

225 g (8 oz) canned, chopped tomatoes

1 teaspoon tomato purée

½ teaspoon chilli sauce

½ small yellow pepper, de-seeded and
   chopped finely

1 celery stick, sliced thinly

1 small courgette, diced

50 g (1¾ oz) small button mushrooms,
   quartered

1 tablespoon shredded fresh basil

salt and freshly ground black pepper

1 teaspoon grated Parmesan cheese,
   to serve (optional)

1. Cook the pasta in a small saucepan of lightly salted, boiling water for 8–10 minutes, until tender. Drain well.

2. Meanwhile, place the chopped tomatoes in a medium saucepan and stir in the tomato purée, chilli sauce, pepper, celery, courgette and mushrooms. Season to taste and bring to the boil. Reduce the heat and simmer, uncovered, for 10 minutes.

3. Mix the cooked pasta and basil into the tomato sauce. Heat through for 2 minutes and then transfer the mixture to a warmed serving bowl. Scatter the top with grated Parmesan cheese, if you want to use it.

try this: *If you wish to have this cold, allow the pasta to cool and then pack it into a plastic container with a tightly fitting lid. Keep it in the fridge until you require a portable lunchtime treat!*

Teriyaki beef noodles

19½ Points per recipe | **Takes 20 minutes + 30 minutes marinating + 10 minutes standing**

Serves 4. Calories per serving 355. Freeze ✓

Teriyaki sauce is widely available from supermarkets, you'll find it near the soy sauce section.

4 tablespoons Teriyaki sauce	225 g (8 oz) medium egg noodles
3 tablespoons tomato ketchup	low fat cooking spray
2 garlic cloves, chopped	1 red onion, sliced
350 g (12 oz) rump steak, trimmed of any fat	225 g (8 oz) savoy cabbage, shredded finely
and cut into thin strips	150 g (5½ oz) sugar snap peas

1. Mix together the Teriyaki sauce, tomato ketchup and garlic in a shallow non-metallic dish. Place the strips of steak in this mixture. Mix well and leave to marinate for 30 minutes.

2. Meanwhile, place the noodles in a bowl and pour boiling water over them. Leave them to stand for 10 minutes and then drain well.

3. Drain the beef, but reserve the marinade. Spray a large non stick wok or frying pan with low fat cooking spray, and stir fry the beef for 5 minutes over a high heat. Add the onion, cabbage and sugar snap peas, and stir fry for a further 2 minutes.

4. Add the noodles and the reserved marinade to the pan. Heat through for 5 minutes and then serve.

tips: *When you soak the noodles it softens them up, so they need hardly any cooking time. However, if you are in a hurry, just cook the noodles in boiling water for 2–3 minutes, and then drain and add to the stir fry as in step 4.*

To give this dish a more intense flavour, marinate the beef overnight in the fridge so the flavours get really absorbed.

Kidney bean pilaff

23½ Points per recipe | **Takes 25 minutes to prepare, 40 minutes to cook**

Ⓥ *Serves 4. Calories per serving 355. Freeze ✓*

Brown rice takes longer to cook than white, but has a delicious nutty texture and is high in fibre so it fills you up more.

For the rice:	For the pesto:
225 g (8 oz) brown rice	25 g (1 oz) flat leaf parsley
1 onion, chopped	finely grated zest and juice of 1 lemon
600 ml (20 fl oz) vegetable stock	1 tablespoon olive oil
2 tablespoons tomato purée	15 g (½ oz) ground almonds
420 g can of red kidney beans, rinsed	1 tablespoon grated Parmesan cheese
and drained	salt and freshly ground black pepper

1. Place the rice in a large saucepan with the chopped onion and stock, and bring to the boil. Reduce the heat, cover and simmer for 35–40 minutes, until the rice is tender.

2. Drain the rice well, and mix in the tomato purée and red kidney beans. In a clean pan, heat the rice mixture gently to warm it through.

3. Meanwhile, make the pesto. Remove any tough stalks from the parsley and chop the leaves finely. Mix it together with the lemon zest and juice, olive oil, ground almonds, Parmesan cheese and seasoning. Add the pesto to the rice mixture. Stir well and heat through. Serve this pilaff hot, or chill it in the fridge and serve it cold as a rice salad.

tip: *Make up a double batch of this pesto and use it to top grilled lean pork or beef steaks.*

Spicy spaghetti bolognese

19½ Points per recipe | Takes 25 minutes to prepare, 30 minutes to cook

Serves 4. Calories per serving 345. Freeze ✓

We've spiced up this all time favourite with a hint of chilli.

---

225 g (8 oz) extra lean minced beef

1 onion, chopped

1 garlic clove, crushed

150 g (5½ oz) mushrooms, sliced

1 cooking apple, peeled and grated

150 g (5½ oz) carrots, grated

1 teaspoon hot chilli powder or cayenne pepper

1 teaspoon ground coriander

2 tablespoons tomato purée

400 g can of chopped tomatoes

225 g (8 oz) spaghetti

salt and freshly ground black pepper

---

1. Heat a large, heavy based non stick frying pan and add the mince. Dry fry it for 5 minutes until it is evenly browned. Add the onion, garlic, mushrooms, apple, carrots, chilli powder or cayenne pepper and ground coriander, and cook for a further 5 minutes.

2. Stir in the tomato purée, chopped tomatoes and 4 tablespoons of water, and bring to the boil. Cover, reduce the heat and simmer for 30 minutes, stirring from time to time.

3. Meanwhile, cook the spaghetti in a large saucepan of lightly salted, boiling water for 8–10 minutes until tender. Drain well.

4. Mix the cooked spaghetti into the bolognese mixture, season and heat through to serve.

tip: *It is important to add a little sweetness to a bolognese sauce as the tomatoes can be a little acidic. In this recipe the grated apple and carrot add sweetness, using natural fruit sugar rather than ordinary sugar.*

try this ⓥ *For a vegetarian version, use 225 g (8 oz) Quorn mince instead of the beef mince. It doesn't need to be browned first. The Points per serving will then be 3½.*

Linguine with smoked ham and peas

17½ Points per recipe | Takes 25 minutes

Serves 4. Calories per serving 325. Freeze ✗

A tasty and simple dish for all the family.

---

225 g (8 oz) linguine

2 teaspoons olive oil

100 g (3½ oz) wafer thin smoked ham, shredded

125 g (4½ oz) frozen peas

100 g (3½ oz) stoned black olives

450 g (1 lb) plum tomatoes, peeled, de-seeded and chopped finely

zest of ½ orange

2 tablespoons chopped fresh flat leaf parsley

salt and freshly ground black pepper

---

1. Cook the pasta in a large saucepan of lightly salted, boiling water for 8–10 minutes or according to the packet instructions. Drain thoroughly and mix with the olive oil.

2. Place the pasta in a large saucepan and add the ham, peas, black olives, chopped tomatoes, orange zest, parsley and seasoning. Heat through while mixing everything together.

3. Divide the pasta mixture between four warmed plates and serve immediately.

tip: *If you are in a hurry, use a can of chopped tomatoes instead of skinning and de-seeding fresh ones.*

try this: *Use spaghetti or tagliatelle instead of linguine for this recipe if you prefer.*

Quorn and mushroom tagliatelle

13 Points per recipe | **Takes 20 minutes**

V *Serves 2. Calories per serving 600. Freeze* ✓

A tasty, filling dish that really is so quick to prepare – perfect for those busy days when you don't have much time to spend in the kitchen.

200 g (7 oz) fresh tagliatelle	2 tablespoons soy sauce
2 teaspoons sunflower oil	150 ml (5 fl oz) skimmed milk
2 shallots, sliced	150 g (5½ oz) low fat soft cheese with garlic
275 g (9½ oz) mushrooms, sliced	and herbs
225 g (8 oz) Quorn pieces	salt and freshly ground black pepper

1. Cook the tagliatelle in a large saucepan of lightly salted, boiling water for 2–3 minutes until tender. Drain well.
2. Meanwhile, heat the oil in a non stick frying pan and cook the shallots, mushrooms and Quorn for 5 minutes, until they are softened. Add the soy sauce, milk and soft cheese. Heat gently, stirring, until the cheese and milk form a creamy sauce – do not overcook, or the mixture may curdle and begin to separate.
3. Mix in the drained pasta and divide between two warmed serving dishes. Season with freshly ground black pepper.

try this: *For a non-vegetarian alternative, use cubes of chicken instead of the Quorn. You will need to stir fry the chicken for a little longer to make sure it's cooked through. Points per serving will be 6½.*

Mushroom and ricotta cannelloni

22 Points per recipe | **Takes 35 minutes to prepare, 25 minutes to cook**

V *Serves 4. Calories per serving 370. Freeze* ✓

Try using a mixture of mushrooms such as button, oyster and shiitake to add extra flavour to the finished dish.

low fat cooking spray	200 g (7 oz) ricotta cheese
1 red onion, chopped	225 g (8 oz) no pre cook cannelloni tubes
1 garlic clove, crushed	400 g can of chopped tomatoes with herbs
450 g (1 lb) mushrooms, chopped finely	150 ml (5 fl oz) passata
200 g (7 oz) baby spinach leaves	salt and freshly ground black pepper
a pinch of ground nutmeg	

1. Heat a frying pan and spray it with low fat cooking spray. Cook the onion, garlic and mushrooms for 5 minutes until softened. Add the spinach and nutmeg, and cook for a few more minutes until the spinach wilts.
2. Remove the pan from the heat, season to taste and beat in the ricotta cheese.
3. Preheat the oven to Gas Mark 5/190°C/fan oven 170°C.
4. Pack the spinach and ricotta filling into the cannelloni shells, and then arrange the shells in a shallow ovenproof dish.
5. Mix the chopped tomatoes with the passata and pour this over the cannelloni. Bake for 25 minutes.

tip: *The easiest way to fill the cannelloni shells is with a small teaspoon, but cover the other end of the shell with your hand, being careful not to burn yourself, to prevent the filling falling out.*

try this: *If you prefer, you can use eight cooked lasagne sheets to wrap around the filling, instead of cannelloni shells, remembering to adjust the Points accordingly.*

Roasted vegetable pasta

13½ Points per recipe | Takes 30 minutes

V **Vg** *Serves 4. Calories per serving 305. Freeze* ✓

1 red onion, cut into thin wedges	1 teaspoon dried oregano
225 g (8 oz) courgettes, cut into chunks	1 tablespoon olive oil
1 aubergine, diced	1 teaspoon balsamic vinegar
1 red pepper, de-seeded and cut into chunks	225 g (8 oz) pasta twists
1 green pepper, de-seeded and cut into chunks	350 g (12 oz) cherry tomatoes, halved
3 garlic cloves, sliced thinly	salt and freshly ground black pepper

1. Preheat the oven to Gas Mark 6/200°C/fan oven 180°C.

2. Arrange the onion wedges, courgettes, aubergine and peppers in a roasting tin. Sprinkle over the garlic, oregano and seasoning. Drizzle the olive oil and balsamic vinegar over the vegetables.

3. Roast for 30 minutes, tossing the vegetables half way through cooking.

4. Cook the pasta in a large saucepan of lightly salted, boiling water for 10–12 minutes, until tender.

5. Add the halved cherry tomatoes to the vegetables and return to the oven for 5 minutes.

6. Finally, mix the cooked vegetables and pasta together and pile it all into a warmed serving dish.

try this: *For a moister mixture, use a can of chopped tomatoes and stir it in to the cooked vegetables instead of the cherry tomatoes. The Points will remain the same.*

tip: *Roasted vegetables make an excellent topping for toast – almost like a mini pizza! Keep a bowl of roast vegetables in the fridge for a handy low Point snack.*

Spaghetti with mussels

11½ Points per recipe | Takes 20 minutes

Serves 2. Calories per serving 440. Freeze ✗

For this dish serve the mussels in their shells, as the plump orange flesh looks so attractive against the black shells. However, if you are worried that they will be awkward to eat, remove the shells first.

175 g (6 oz) spaghetti	3 tablespoons dry white wine
1 teaspoon olive oil	450 g (1 lb) fresh mussels, scrubbed
3 shallots, chopped finely	salt and freshly ground black pepper
1 garlic clove, crushed	2 tablespoons chopped fresh parsley,
1 fresh red chilli, de-seeded and chopped finely	to garnish

1. Cook the spaghetti in a large saucepan of lightly salted, boiling water until tender. This will take 8–10 minutes.

2. Meanwhile, heat the olive oil in a pan and add the shallots, garlic and chilli. Cook over a low heat for 2–3 minutes until they are softened. Then add the dry white wine, mussels and seasoning. Make sure you discard any open mussels that do not close when tapped.

3. Cover the pan and cook for 5 minutes until the mussel shells have opened. Once cooked discard any mussels that haven't opened.

4. Drain the spaghetti and mix it with the cooked mussels and their pan juices. Pile into two warmed serving bowls and garnish with chopped fresh parsley.

tip: *To reduce the Points you could omit the white wine. The Points per serving will then be 5½.*

Chicken lasagne

26 Points per recipe | Takes 45 minutes to prepare, 25 minutes to cook

Serves 4. Calories per serving 415. Freeze ✓

2 teaspoons olive oil	150 ml (5 fl oz) boiling water
350 g (12 oz) skinless chicken breasts, cut into bite size chunks	8 sheets no pre cook lasagne sheets
450 g (1 lb) leeks, sliced thinly	300 ml (10 fl oz) skimmed milk
1 garlic clove, crushed	25 g (1 oz) cornflour
400 g can of chopped tomatoes	200 g (7 oz) low fat soft cheese
2 tablespoons tomato purée	25 g (1 oz) Parmesan cheese, grated
1 teaspoon dried basil	salt and freshly ground black pepper

1. Heat the oil in a non stick frying pan and add the chicken, leeks and garlic. Stir fry for 5 minutes until the chicken begins to brown.

2. Add the chopped tomatoes, tomato purée, basil, seasoning and the boiling water. Simmer for 15 minutes.

3. Preheat the oven to Gas Mark 5/190°C/fan oven 170°C.

4. Spoon half the chicken and leek mixture into a deep, ovenproof rectangular dish, and then arrange four sheets of lasagne on top. Spoon on the remaining chicken mixture and finish with the last four lasagne sheets.

5. Heat the milk until it is boiling. In a bowl, mix the cornflour to a thin paste with a little cold water. Pour the boiling milk into the bowl and then return this mixture to a clean pan and cook, whisking, until it thickens. Stir in the low fat soft cheese and then pour this cheese sauce over the top of the lasagne sheets.

6. Sprinkle the surface with the Parmesan cheese and bake in the oven for 25 minutes.

tip: *Lasagne is always a good standby meal to have at hand. It freezes well, so wrap up any leftovers in individual portions and pop them in the freezer for another day.*

try this: *You can use 350 g (12 oz) turkey mince for the filling instead of chopped chicken, if you prefer – it will make this dish a little less expensive. The Points per serving will be 7.*

Pasta with baby vegetables and cheese

15 Points per recipe | Takes 30 minutes

V *Serves 2. Calories per serving 445. Freeze ✓*

125 g (4½ oz) pasta bows	15 g (½ oz) pine nut kernels
175 g (6 oz) baby leeks, sliced	75 g (2¾ oz) feta cheese, crumbled
100 g (3½ oz) petits pois	finely grated zest of ½ lemon
300 ml (10 fl oz) vegetable stock	salt and freshly ground black pepper

1. Cook the pasta in a large saucepan of lightly salted, boiling water for 8–10 minutes according to the packet instructions. Drain well.

2. Meanwhile, in a small saucepan, cook the leeks and petits pois in the stock for 5 minutes. Drain well, reserving 3 tablespoons of the liquid.

3. Heat a small pan and add the pine nut kernels. Dry fry for 2–3 minutes until they begin to turn golden.

4. Mix the cooked pasta and vegetables together with the reserved cooking liquid, feta cheese, toasted pine nut kernels, lemon zest and seasoning. This dish is at its best served straight away as the heat of the pasta and vegetables will begin to melt the feta cheese, giving it a wonderfully creamy texture.

Chicken lasagne

Macaroni cheese and tuna bake

24½ Points per recipe | **Takes 30 minutes to prepare, 20 minutes to cook**

Serves 4. Calories per serving 425. Freeze ✓

A great midweek meal which all the family will enjoy.

---

25 g (1 oz) low fat spread

25 g (1 oz) plain white flour

300 ml (10 fl oz) skimmed milk

150 g (5½ oz) low fat soft cheese with
   garlic and herbs

100 g (3½ oz) frozen peas

100 g (3½ oz) frozen sweetcorn

1 red pepper, de-seeded and diced

200 g (7 oz) canned tuna in brine, drained
   and flaked

225 g (8 oz) quick cook macaroni

2 tomatoes, sliced

1 teaspoon dried oregano

salt and freshly ground black pepper

---

1. Preheat the oven to Gas Mark 5/190°C/fan oven 170°C.

2. Gently heat the low fat spread in a small heavy based saucepan and stir in the flour. Gradually add the milk, whisking until you have a smooth, thickened sauce. Remove from the heat and stir in the low fat soft cheese. Add in the peas, sweetcorn, red pepper, tuna and seasoning.

3. Cook the macaroni in a large saucepan of lightly salted, boiling water according to the packet instructions. Drain thoroughly and fold it into the tuna sauce.

4. Transfer the macaroni to an ovenproof dish and arrange the tomato slices on top. Sprinkle over the oregano and bake for 20 minutes.

tip: *Take care when making a sauce with low fat spread, you will need to whisk it continuously while adding the milk as it easily turns lumpy. If it starts getting a little lumpy, remove the pan from the heat and whisk the sauce vigorously for a few seconds with electric beaters or a balloon whisk.*

Sesame noodles with red cabbage

14 Points per recipe | **Takes 20 minutes**

V *Serves 4. Calories per serving 240. Freeze ✓*

This tasty snack is a wonderful accompaniment to grilled meat or fish.

---

225 g (8 oz) medium egg noodles

low fat cooking spray

1 red onion, sliced

350 g (12 oz) red cabbage, shredded finely

finely grated zest and juice of 1 orange

15 g (½ oz) sesame seeds

1 teaspoon sesame oil, to serve

---

1. Place the noodles in a large bowl and cover them with boiling water. Leave them to stand for 10 minutes, stirring from time to time.

2. Meanwhile, spray a large frying pan or wok with low fat cooking spray, and add the red onion and cabbage. Stir fry for 5 minutes until the vegetables begin to soften.

3. Drain the noodles thoroughly. Add them to the pan with the orange zest and juice and sesame seeds. Stir fry for a further 2–3 minutes, until everything is piping hot. Drizzle with sesame oil just before serving.

tip: *Sesame oil is strong in flavour, so a little goes a long way. However, it burns even at a low temperature which makes it unsuitable for cooking; it's best used as a flavouring.*

try this: *Add 225 g (8 oz) cubed tofu for a more substantial dish. The Points will then be 4 per serving.*

Sweet and sour pork noodles

22 Points per recipe | Takes 40 minutes

Serves 4. Calories per serving 395. Freeze ✓

225 g (8 oz) medium egg noodles	3 tablespoons soy sauce
1 teaspoon sesame oil	2 tablespoons tomato purée
low fat cooking spray	1 tablespoon cornflour
350 g (12 oz) pork tenderloin, cut into thin strips	1 teaspoon wine vinegar
2 garlic cloves, crushed	1 green pepper, de-seeded and sliced
225 g (8 oz) canned pineapple chunks in natural juice	150 g (5½ oz) carrots, cut into matchsticks
	150 g (5½ oz) courgettes, sliced

1. Cook the noodles in a large saucepan of lightly salted, boiling water for 2 minutes. Drain well and mix in the sesame oil. Set aside.

2. Spray a large non stick frying pan or wok with low fat cooking spray, and stir fry the pork and garlic for 5 minutes.

3. Drain the pineapple, reserving the juice. Add the pineapple chunks to the pan.

4. Mix the reserved juice with the soy sauce, tomato purée, cornflour and vinegar to make a sweet and sour mixture, and set aside.

5. Add the pepper, carrots and courgettes to the pan and stir fry for a further 5 minutes. Stir in the sweet and sour sauce and cook, stirring, until the sauce thickens.

6. Add the cooked noodles to the pan and heat through for 2–3 minutes. Serve on four warmed plates.

tips: *When you need to slice meat really thinly, freeze it for about half an hour beforehand and it will be much easier to handle.*

This dish freezes well; divide it into individual portions and pop in the freezer for when you want a quick and easy meal.

try this: *Add a teaspoon of hot chilli sauce to the sweet and sour mixture for an added zing with no extra Points.*

Spicy gammon and bean hot pot

18 Points per recipe | Takes 15 minutes to prepare, 25 minutes to cook

Serves 4. Calories per serving 330. Freeze ✓

There is an extensive range of canned beans and pulses available today, and they are relatively low in Points. Try and include them in your cooking as they make meals more filling and are good for you, too.

low fat cooking spray	400 g can of mixed beans in chilli sauce
350 g (12 oz) lean gammon steak, diced	150 ml (5 fl oz) apple juice
225 g (8 oz) leeks, sliced	1 tablespoon wholegrain mustard
225 g (8 oz) carrots, diced	salt and freshly ground black pepper
400 g can of chopped tomatoes	

1. Spray a large saucepan with low fat cooking spray and cook the gammon over a high heat for 2–3 minutes.

2. Add the remaining ingredients and bring to the boil. Reduce the heat, cover and simmer for 20–25 minutes, until the leeks and carrots are cooked. Serve hot.

try this: *You may find the apple juice a little too sweet. If this is the case use vegetable or chicken stock instead. The Points will be reduced to 4 per serving.*

Chilli crab noodles

12½ Points per recipe | Takes 20 minutes

Serves 2. Calories per serving 455. Freeze ✗

When time is of the essence, create this tasty dish from start to finish in less than 20 minutes.

150 g (5½ oz) vermicelli noodles

2 teaspoons sunflower oil

1 small red pepper, de-seeded and sliced
  thinly

100 g (3½ oz) baby sweetcorn, halved

6 spring onions, sliced

200 g (7 oz) canned white crab meat,
  drained

2 tablespoons sweet chilli sauce

2 tablespoons tomato ketchup

1 tablespoon soy sauce

2 tablespoons chopped fresh coriander,
  to serve

1. Place the noodles in a bowl and cover them with boiling water. Leave them to stand for 5 minutes and then drain thoroughly.

2. Meanwhile, heat the oil in a pan and stir fry the red pepper and baby sweetcorn for 2–3 minutes. Add the drained noodles, spring onions, crab meat, sweet chilli sauce, tomato ketchup and soy sauce, and stir fry for 2–3 minutes.

3. Scatter over the chopped fresh coriander and serve.

tips: *Vermicelli noodles can go very soggy if left standing around for too long, so serve this dish immediately and avoid over soaking the noodles – 5 minutes is plenty of time as they are thinner than ordinary noodles.*

Canned crab meat comes wrapped in paper; to drain it remove it from the can and squeeze the excess liquid out gently. Don't squeeze too much or you'll be left with very dry flakes.

Quick and easy supper for two

This exciting meal is ready in no time at all and it tastes absolutely fantastic.

Chilli crab noodles *above*, 1 serving......................6 Points
(pictured left)

Boozy sticky toffee bananas, *page 181*, 1 serving ...3½ Points

Total Points for meal ....9½ **Points**

Oyster mushroom noodles

13½ Points per recipe | Takes 25 minutes

Serves 4. Calories per serving 265. Freeze ✓

This dish is great either on its own or as an accompaniment to grilled chicken breasts.

250 g (9 oz) medium egg noodles	3 tablespoons oyster sauce
low fat cooking spray	100 ml (3½ fl oz) beef stock
450 g (1 lb) oyster mushrooms, sliced	1 teaspoon cornflour
2 garlic cloves, crushed	2 tablespoons dry sherry
6 spring onions, sliced	

1. Place the noodles in a bowl and cover them with boiling water. Leave them to stand for 10 minutes, stirring occasionally.

2. Spray a large frying pan with low fat cooking spray and stir fry the mushrooms and garlic for 5 minutes, until softened.

3. Drain the noodles and then add them to the pan with the spring onions, oyster sauce and stock. Bring to the boil and cook, stirring, for 2 minutes.

4. Mix the cornflour to a paste with the sherry and drizzle this into the pan. Cook, stirring, for 2 minutes until the sauce thickens. Serve hot.

tip: *Oyster mushrooms are quite delicate, so take care when stir frying or they may break up.*

try this: Ⓥ *For a vegetarian version of this dish with the same Points, use soy sauce instead of oyster sauce, and vegetable stock.*

Chinese ginger noodles

18½ Points per recipe | Takes 25 minutes

Ⓥ *Serves 4. Calories per serving 360. Freeze ✓*

Serve this dish as soon as you make it otherwise the noodles soak up too much of the sauce and become stodgy.

225 g (8 oz) thin egg noodles	6 spring onions, sliced into long, thin strips
2 teaspoons vegetable oil	150 g (5½ oz) fresh beansprouts
225 g (8 oz) carrots, cut into matchsticks	100 ml (3½ fl oz) vegetable stock
5 cm (2 inch) piece of root ginger, peeled and grated	1 teaspoon cornflour
2 garlic cloves, chopped	2 tablespoons soy sauce
225 g (8 oz) firm tofu, diced	1 tablespoon tomato purée
	25 g (1 oz) cashew nuts, chopped roughly

1. Place the noodles in a bowl and cover them with boiling water. Leave to stand for 10 minutes, stirring from time to time to separate the noodles.

2. Heat the oil in a large non stick frying pan or wok, and add the carrots, ginger and garlic. Stir fry for 2–3 minutes and then mix in the tofu, spring onions and beansprouts. Stir fry for a further 2 minutes.

3. Drain the noodles and add them to the pan with the stock. Mix well and heat through for 2 minutes.

4. Mix together the cornflour, soy sauce and tomato purée, and add this to the pan. Cook, stirring, until the sauce thickens.

5. Pile into a warmed serving bowl and scatter with chopped cashew nuts. Serve hot.

tip: *Keep a piece of root ginger in the freezer and you'll always have some to hand; it also grates more easily when frozen.*

vegetarian...
dishes

Carrot and butter bean terrine

13 Points per recipe | **Takes 45 minutes to prepare, 1 hour to cook**

V *Serves 4. Calories per serving 250. Freeze* ✓

This colourful terrine is delicious eaten hot or cold. Serve it with a simple, zero Point, sliced tomato salad drizzled with balsamic vinegar.

---

700 g (1 lb 9 oz) carrots, diced

1 onion, chopped

1 garlic clove, crushed

600 ml (20 fl oz) vegetable stock

1 teaspoon ground coriander

2 large eggs

25 g (1 oz) fresh white or wholemeal breadcrumbs

420 g can of butter beans, drained and rinsed

150 g (5½ oz) low fat soft cheese with garlic and herbs

salt and freshly ground black pepper

---

1. Place the carrots, onion, garlic and stock in a large saucepan, and bring to the boil. Add the ground coriander and seasoning. Cover and simmer for 15 minutes until the carrots are tender.

2. Drain well and mash thoroughly or blend in a food processor. Beat in the eggs and stir in the breadcrumbs.

3. Line a 900 g (2 lb) loaf tin with non stick baking parchment. Spoon half the mixture into the tin.

4. Mash the butter beans with the low fat soft cheese or blend them together in a food processor. Spread this over the carrot mixture in the tin. Top with the remaining carrot mixture.

5. Cover the terrine with a sheet of non stick baking parchment, and then cover the whole tin with foil.

6. Place the tin in a large saucepan or wok and pour in enough water to come half way up the sides of the tin. Bring the water to the boil, cover and reduce the heat. Alternatively, place the tin in a roasting tray with water and bake at Gas Mark 5/190°C/fan oven 170°C. Simmer gently for 1 hour. Check the water level from time to time and top up with boiling water if necessary.

7. Carefully lift the tin out of the water, remove the foil and baking parchment and let it cool.

8. Run a round bladed knife around the edge of the terrine to loosen the edges. Place a serving platter on top of the tin, and then turn the tin upside down so the terrine drops out on to the platter. Cut it into eight slices and serve two slices per person.

Zero Point casserole

0 Points per recipe | Takes 15 minutes to prepare, 35 minutes to cook

V **Vg** *Serves 4. Calories per serving 100. Freeze ✓*

Fill up on a bowl of this tasty zero Point casserole, or have some before going out to eat to stave off those hunger pangs – you're then less likely to over indulge.

---

225 g (8 oz) carrots, sliced

350 g (12 oz) turnips, diced

4 celery sticks, sliced

1 red onion, chopped

2 garlic cloves, crushed

150 g (5½ oz) fine green beans, halved

350 g (12 oz) cauliflower, broken into florets

1 teaspoon paprika

1 teaspoon ground coriander

300 ml (10 fl oz) vegetable stock

400 g can of chopped tomatoes with herbs

salt and freshly ground black pepper

---

1. Place the carrots, turnips, celery, red onion, garlic, green beans and cauliflower in a large saucepan.

2. Sprinkle over the paprika and coriander, and stir the vegetables to coat them evenly in the spices. Add the stock and stir in the chopped tomatoes. Season to taste.

3. Bring the pan to the boil. Reduce the heat, cover and simmer for 30 minutes until the vegetables are tender.

4. Remove the cover, turn up the heat and allow the mixture to bubble vigorously for 5 minutes to reduce some of the liquid. Serve on four warmed plates.

tip: *The cauliflower will break down quite a bit after 30 minutes cooking and helps to thicken the casserole. If you prefer your cauliflower with a bit more bite, add it to the pan for the last 15 minutes of cooking time.*

goes well with...

two medium slices of crusty French stick, for an extra 3 Points per serving.

Sweet potato and red leicester strudel

15 Points per recipe | **Takes 40 minutes to prepare, 20 minutes to cook**

V *Serves 4. Calories per serving 270. Freeze* ✓

450 g (1 lb) sweet potatoes, peeled and diced	1 onion, chopped finely
75 g (2¾ oz) half fat Red Leicester cheese, grated	4 sheets filo pastry
1 red pepper, de-seeded and diced	1 tablespoon olive oil
	salt and freshly ground black pepper

1. Cook the sweet potatoes in a large saucepan of lightly salted, boiling water, until tender. This will take about 10 minutes.

2. Drain the potatoes and mash them thoroughly. Mix in the cheese, red pepper, onion and seasoning. Allow the mixture to cool for 10 minutes.

3. Preheat the oven to Gas Mark 5/190°C/fan oven 170°C.

4. Brush each sheet of filo pastry lightly with some of the olive oil and stack them one on top of each other. Spread the sweet potato mixture over the top of the stack to within 2 cm (¾ inch) of the edges. Carefully roll up the pastry to enclose the filling.

5. Lift the roll of pastry on to a non stick baking tray and brush it with the remaining oil. Gently score the top with a sharp knife. Bake for 20 minutes until the pastry is crisp and golden. Cut the strudel into four slices and serve.

try this: *Red Leicester cheese has a wonderfully rich, deep orange colour that goes very well with the sweet potato, but you can use half fat Cheddar cheese if you prefer the flavour. The Points will remain the same.*

Shepherdess pie

22 Points per recipe | **Takes 35 minutes to prepare, 20 minutes to cook**

V *Serves 4. Calories per serving 250. Freeze* ✓

This Shepherdess pie freezes very well, so divide it into portions and freeze, ready for a speedy supper.

450 g (1 lb) potatoes, peeled and diced	150 g (5½ oz) mushrooms, chopped finely
225 g (8 oz) parsnips, diced	350 g (12 oz) vegetarian mince
3 tablespoons half fat crème fraîche	300 ml (10 fl oz) vegetable stock
low fat cooking spray	2 tablespoons dark soy sauce
1 onion, chopped	1 tablespoon tomato purée
1 garlic clove, crushed	1 tablespoon cornflour
150 g (5½ oz) carrots, grated	salt and freshly ground black pepper

1. Cook the potatoes and parsnips in lightly salted, boiling water for 15 minutes until tender. Drain well and mash them with the crème fraîche and seasoning.

2. Meanwhile, spray a large saucepan with low fat cooking spray and add the onion, garlic, carrots and mushrooms. Cook, stirring, for 5 minutes and then stir in the vegetarian mince.

3. Add the stock, soy sauce and tomato purée to the pan and bring to the boil. Cover and simmer for 10 minutes.

4. Preheat the oven to Gas Mark 5/190°C/fan oven 170°C. Mix the cornflour with a little cold water to make a thin paste and stir this into the mince and vegetable mixture. Cook, stirring, until the sauce thickens a little.

5. Transfer the mince mixture to an ovenproof dish and top with the potato and parsnip mash. Bake in the oven for 20 minutes.

try this: *The strong sweet flavour of parsnips gives extra flavour to the mash. If you're not a fan of parsnips, try using sweet potatoes instead. The Points per serving will remain the same.*

Lentil moussaka

22½ Points per recipe | Takes 50 minutes to prepare, 30 minutes to cook

(v) *Serves 4. Calories per serving 395. Freeze ✔*

This version of a classic Greek dish is a meal in itself or you could serve it with a crisp green zero Point salad.

2 teaspoons olive oil	1 aubergine, sliced thinly
1 onion, chopped	25 g (1 oz) polyunsaturated margarine
2 garlic cloves, crushed	25 g (1 oz) plain white flour
150 g (5½ oz) dried, split red lentils	300 ml (10 fl oz) skimmed milk
300 ml (10 fl oz) vegetable stock	a pinch of ground nutmeg
1 teaspoon dried marjoram	25 g (1 oz) Parmesan cheese, grated
420 g can of chopped tomatoes	1 beefsteak tomato, sliced
2 tablespoons tomato purée	salt and freshly ground black pepper
450 g (1 lb) potatoes, peeled and sliced thinly (5 mm/¼ inch)	

1. Heat the olive oil in a large saucepan, and add the onion and garlic. Cover and cook over a low heat for about 8–10 minutes until the onion has softened, but not browned.

2. Stir in the lentils, stock, marjoram, chopped tomatoes, tomato purée and seasoning, and bring to the boil. Cover and simmer for 25 minutes, stirring from time to time, until the lentils are tender and have absorbed most of the liquid.

3. Meanwhile, cook the potato slices in lightly salted, boiling water for 10 minutes, until tender. Drain well and set aside.

4. Cook the aubergine slices in lightly salted, boiling water for 5 minutes. Drain well and set aside.

5. Heat the margarine in a small saucepan and stir in the flour. Gradually add the milk and cook, stirring, until you have a smooth sauce. Beat in the nutmeg and Parmesan cheese.

6. Preheat the oven to Gas Mark 4/180°C/fan oven 160°C. Spoon the lentil mixture into an ovenproof dish and top with the sliced potatoes followed by the aubergine. Spoon the cheese sauce over the top.

7. Top with tomato slices and bake in the oven for 30 minutes. Cut the moussaka into squares to serve.

Plum tomato and olive pizza

19 Points per recipe | Takes 35 minutes to prepare, 20 minutes to cook

(v) *Serves 4. Calories per serving 235. Freeze ✔*

Next time you get the urge for a takeaway pizza, make this fabulous recipe and save some valuable Points.

200 g (7 oz) pizza base mix	50 g (1¾ oz) stoned black olives, halved
900 g (2 lb) plum tomatoes, halved	2 tablespoons shredded fresh basil
1 teaspoon salt	100 g (3½ oz) mozzarella light, sliced thinly
2 tablespoons tomato purée	freshly ground black pepper

1. Preheat the oven to Gas Mark 6/200°C/fan oven 180°C. Make up the pizza base mix according to the packet instructions. Roll the dough out to a 25 cm (10 inch) circle. Lift the dough on to a non stick baking tray, cover with a damp tea towel and leave to prove for 30 minutes.

2. Meanwhile, arrange the tomatoes cut side up on a baking tray and season with the salt and some freshly ground black pepper. Roast for 25 minutes.

3. Spread the pizza base with tomato purée and arrange the roasted tomatoes on top. Scatter over the olives and basil. Top with slices of mozzarella and bake for 20 minutes, until the cheese has melted. Serve cut into wedges.

Quorn and pepper lasagne

17 Points per recipe | **Takes 30 minutes to prepare, 25 minutes to cook**

V *Serves 4. Calories per serving 330. Freeze ✓*

low fat cooking spray	2 tablespoons tomato purée
1 onion, chopped	1 teaspoon dried basil
1 garlic clove, crushed	150 g (5½ oz) no pre-cook lasagne sheets
1 red pepper, de-seeded and diced	300 ml (10 fl oz) skimmed milk
1 green pepper, de-seeded and diced	2 tablespoons cornflour
225 g (8 oz) Quorn mince	100 g (3½ oz) low fat soft cheese with garlic
1 vegetable stock cube, crumbled	and herbs
420 g can of chopped tomatoes with herbs	salt and freshly ground black pepper

1. Spray a large saucepan with low fat cooking spray and add the onion, garlic and peppers. Cook over a low heat for 5 minutes until the vegetables soften. Stir in the Quorn mince and stock cube, and cook for a further 2 minutes.
2. Stir in the chopped tomatoes, tomato purée, dried basil and seasoning, and bring to the boil. Reduce the heat and simmer for 5 minutes.
3. Soak the lasagne sheets in boiling water for 5 minutes.
4. Reserve 2 tablespoons of milk and heat the rest until it is just boiling. Mix the reserved milk with the cornflour to make a paste. Pour the hot milk over the paste and return the mixture to a clean pan. Cook, stirring, until the sauce thickens. Remove the pan from the heat and whisk in the soft cheese.
5. Preheat the oven to Gas Mark 5/190°C/fan oven 170°C. Spoon half the Quorn mixture into a rectangular ovenproof dish, top with half the lasagne sheets and half the cheese sauce.
6. Repeat the layers, finishing with a layer of cheese sauce. Bake for 25 minutes and serve hot.

tip: *Soaking the lasagne sheets prevents them absorbing too much liquid when they are in the oven, making sure that the lasagne doesn't dry out during cooking.*

Zero Point vegetable curry

0 Points per recipe | **Takes 15 minutes to prepare, 40 minutes to cook**

V **Vg** *Serves 4. Calories per serving 125. Freeze ✓*

1 onion, chopped	175 g (6 oz) button mushrooms, quartered
2 garlic cloves, crushed	2 tablespoons medium curry powder
175 g (6 oz) carrots, sliced	300 ml (10 fl oz) vegetable stock
225 g (8 oz) leeks, sliced	400 g can of chopped tomatoes
225 g (8 oz) courgettes, sliced	salt and freshly ground black pepper
1 aubergine, diced	2 tablespoons chopped fresh coriander,
350 g (12 oz) cauliflower, broken into florets	to garnish
100 g (3½ oz) fine green beans, halved	

1. Place the onion, garlic, carrots, leeks, courgettes, aubergine, cauliflower, green beans and mushrooms in a large saucepan and add the curry powder. Mix well so the vegetables become coated with the curry powder.
2. Stir in the stock and tomatoes, and season to taste. Bring to the boil and then simmer uncovered for 40 minutes, stirring from time to time.
3. Serve the curry sprinkled with chopped fresh coriander.

Red pepper and basil cheesecake

21 Points per recipe | Takes 35 minutes to prepare, 20 minutes to cook + 10 minutes cooling

v *Serves 6. Calories per serving 225. Freeze ✓*

Not all cheesecakes have to be sweet, try this savoury version and you'll be hooked!

For the pastry:

**100 g (3½ oz) plain white flour plus 2
 teaspoons for rolling**

1 tablespoon cornflour

50 g (1¾ oz) polyunsaturated margarine

a pinch of salt

For the filling:

3 red peppers, de-seeded and halved

350 g (12 oz) low fat plain cottage cheese

2 eggs

2 tablespoons torn fresh basil

salt and freshly ground black pepper

1. To make the pastry, mix the flour and cornflour together in a bowl. Rub in the margarine with your fingertips, until the mixture resembles fine breadcrumbs. Add the salt and then stir in enough cold water to make a soft dough.

2. Preheat the oven to Gas Mark 5/190°C/fan oven 170°C. On a lightly floured surface, roll out the pastry so it is big enough to line the base and sides of a 20 cm (8 inch) fluted loose bottomed flan tin.

3. Lift the pastry into the tin and prick the base with a fork. Line with non stick baking parchment and baking beans. Bake blind for 10 minutes. Remove the paper and the beans, and return the pastry to the oven for 10 minutes.

4. Meanwhile, grill the peppers under a high heat, skin side up, until the skins blacken and blister. Transfer the peppers to a polythene bag and seal. When they are cool enough to handle, peel off the skins and roughly chop the flesh.

5. Place the peppers, cottage cheese, eggs, basil and seasoning in a food processor and blend until smooth. Remove the pastry flan case from the oven and spoon in the pepper filling.

6. Return the flan to the oven for 20 minutes, until the filling has set and is firm to the touch. Allow to cool for 10 minutes before slicing into wedges to serve.

tip: *If you don't have a food processor, chop the red pepper very finely and push the cottage cheese through a sieve. Mix them together with the eggs, seasoning and basil as in step 5 before spooning into the flan case.*

Chilli veggie mince wraps

8½ Points per recipe | Takes 20 minutes

v **Vg** *Serves 4. Calories per serving 130. Freeze ✓ (see step 2)*

Great party finger food – these little wraps will make it a real occasion!

1 tablespoon sunflower oil

1 onion, chopped finely

2 garlic cloves, crushed

**5 cm (2 inch) piece of root ginger, peeled
 and grated**

225 g (8 oz) vegetarian mince

1 teaspoon chilli flakes

175 g (6 oz) carrots, grated

175 g (6 oz) courgettes, grated

2 tablespoons tomato purée

2 tablespoons soy sauce

**12 large green lettuce leaves, such as
 Webb's lettuce**

1. Heat the oil in a large frying pan and add the onion, garlic and ginger. Cook over a low heat for 5 minutes, stirring, until the onion softens but doesn't brown.

2. Turn up the heat and add the mince, chilli flakes, carrots, courgettes, tomato purée and soy sauce. Stir fry for 5 minutes until piping hot. If you wish to freeze this, do it now.

3. To serve, spoon a little of the chilli mince mixture on to the centre of each lettuce leaf and wrap like a parcel.

Savoury tarte tatin

19½ Points per recipe | Takes 30 minutes to prepare, 20 minutes to cook

V *Serves 4. Calories per serving 245. Freeze* ✓

The colourful topping of this upside down tart will begin to caramelise as it cooks, giving it a lovely thick glaze.

---

175 g (6 oz) courgettes, sliced

1 red onion, cut into thin wedges

225 g (8 oz) open cup mushrooms, halved

1 garlic clove, crushed

a sprig of fresh rosemary, chopped

1 tablespoon olive oil

1 teaspoon balsamic vinegar

175 g (6 oz) small tomatoes, halved

2 teaspoons plain white flour, for rolling

175 g (6 oz) puff pastry

salt and freshly ground black pepper

---

1. Preheat the oven to Gas Mark 6/200°C/fan oven 180°C.

2. Mix together the courgettes, red onion, mushrooms, garlic, rosemary, olive oil, balsamic vinegar and seasoning. Arrange them on a non stick baking sheet lined with non stick baking parchment and roast for 15 minutes.

3. Remove the vegetables from the oven. Arrange all the vegetables, including the tomatoes, on the base of a 20 cm (8 inch) non stick frying pan or cake tin.

4. Roll out the pastry on a lightly floured surface to make a 23 cm (9 inch) circle. Lay the pastry over the vegetables, tucking in the edges all the way round. Bake the tart in the oven for 20 minutes until the pastry is well risen and golden.

5. Carefully run a round bladed knife around the edge of the pan or tin. Put a large plate over the top and turn the pan or tin upside down, so the tart drops on to the plate. Cut the tart into quarters to serve.

tip: *Make sure that if you are using a frying pan for this recipe it has a metal or ovenproof handle, otherwise use a round cake tin.*

try this: *Use other vegetables, such as de-seeded, diced red or green peppers or cubes of aubergine, in place of any of those used here.*

If you like, replace the olive oil with low fat cooking spray and save 1 Point per serving. Just spray the vegetables when they are on the baking sheet in step 2.

Veggie supper

This delicious, contemporary meal shows just how exciting and satisfying vegetarian dishes can be.

Mushroom and garlic soup *page 15*, 1 serving ....1½ Points

Savoury tarte tatin *above*, 1 serving ....5 Points

Peach and blueberry brûlée *page 173*, 1 serving ....3 Points

Total Points for meal ....**9½ Points**

Chick pea pilau

22½ Points per recipe | Takes 20 minutes

Ⓥ Ⓥg *Serves 4. Calories per serving 415. Freeze* ✓

low fat cooking spray	225 g (8 oz) courgettes, diced
1 onion, chopped finely	227 g can of chopped tomatoes
1 garlic clove, crushed	600 ml (20 fl oz) vegetable stock
300 g (10½ oz) basmati rice	410 g can of chick peas, rinsed and drained
1 teaspoon cumin seeds	150 g (5½ oz) baby spinach leaves, washed
1 teaspoon ground coriander	and drained
½ teaspoon mild chilli powder	2 tablespoons chopped fresh coriander
1 teaspoon paprika	salt and freshly ground black pepper
225 g (8 oz) carrots, diced finely	

1. Spray a large saucepan with low fat cooking spray, and add the onion and garlic. Stir in the rice, cumin seeds, ground coriander, chilli powder and paprika, and cook for 2 minutes.

2. Stir in the carrots, courgettes, tomatoes and stock, and bring to the boil. Cover, reduce the heat and simmer for 10 minutes.

3. Add the chick peas, spinach, fresh coriander and seasoning, and stir well. Cover and cook for a further 2–3 minutes, until the rice is tender and the liquid has been absorbed.

try this: *For a nuttier version, use brown rice instead of basmati. You will need to use an extra 300 ml (10 fl oz) stock and the rice will need 40 minutes cooking time before adding the chick peas, spinach and coriander. The Points will remain the same.*

Pitta pockets with roasted vegetables

6½ Points per recipe | Takes 15 minutes to prepare, 30 minutes to cook

Ⓥ *Serves 2. Calories per serving 255. Freeze* ✗

Pitta breads are a great alternative to bread for any sandwich filling.

125 g (4½ oz) courgettes, cut into chunks	100 g (3½ oz) cherry tomatoes, halved
1 red onion, cut into wedges	75 g (2¾ oz) low fat soft cheese with garlic
½ aubergine, cubed	and herbs, cubed
1 small green pepper, de-seeded and diced	2 medium pitta breads
1 tablespoon balsamic vinegar	salt and freshly ground black pepper
low fat cooking spray	

1. Preheat the oven to Gas Mark 5/190°C/fan oven 170°C. Line a roasting tin with non stick baking parchment.

2. In a large mixing bowl, mix together the courgettes, onion, aubergine and green pepper with the balsamic vinegar and seasoning. Spray with a little low fat cooking spray.

3. Arrange the vegetables in the roasting tin and cook for 25 minutes, turning them half way through. Remove from the oven and mix in the tomatoes and cheese. Return to the oven for 5 minutes.

4. Warm the pitta breads in the oven for the last 5 minutes of the roasting time.

5. Split the warm pittas lengthways. Pile the cooked mixture into the breads and serve.

tip: *Balsamic vinegar can be quite expensive, choose the best you can afford as a little goes a long way. Its sweet, sticky flavour is quite different to ordinary vinegar.*

Falafel with cucumber salsa

12½ Points per recipe | Takes 20 minutes to prepare, 15 minutes to cook

Ⓥ *Serves 4. Calories per serving 145. Freeze ✓ (falafel only)*

For the falafel:

410 g can of chick peas, rinsed and drained

1 garlic clove, crushed

50 g (1¾ oz) wholemeal breadcrumbs

4 spring onions, sliced thinly

1 egg

1 teaspoon ground cumin

low fat cooking spray

salt and freshly ground black pepper

½ Iceberg lettuce, shredded, to serve

For the salsa:

175 g (6 oz) cucumber, diced finely

3 tablespoons chopped fresh coriander

1 tablespoon mint jelly

150 ml (5 fl oz) low fat plain yogurt

1. Preheat the oven to Gas Mark 5/190°C/fan oven 170°C.
2. To make the falafel, place the chick peas, garlic, breadcrumbs, spring onions, egg, cumin and seasoning in a food processor and blend until smooth. If you don't have a food processor, mash the ingredients together thoroughly.
3. Line a baking sheet with non stick baking parchment. Using your hands, shape the chick pea mixture into 20 small balls. Place them on the prepared baking sheet and spray them lightly with low fat cooking spray. Bake for 15 minutes.
4. Meanwhile, make the salsa. Mix together the cucumber, coriander, mint jelly and yogurt and spoon this into four small dishes. Serve five falafel each, hot or cold, on a bed of shredded lettuce with the salsa for dipping.

tip: *Dampen your hands with a little cold water before shaping the falafel, to make the mixture easier to handle.*

try this: *For a more substantial meal, split a warmed medium pitta bread and stuff it with the cooked falafel and lettuce. Drizzle the filled pitta bread with the salsa. This will add 2½ Points per serving.*

Broccoli and blue cheese gratin

23½ Points per recipe | Takes 35 minutes

Ⓥ *Serves 4. Calories per serving 325. Freeze ✓*

350 g (12 oz) baby new potatoes, scrubbed
   and halved

450 g (1 lb) broccoli, broken into florets

25 g (1 oz) polyunsaturated margarine

25 g (1 oz) plain white flour

1 teaspoon English mustard powder

300 ml (10 fl oz) skimmed milk

100 g (3½ oz) blue cheese (e.g. Stilton),
   crumbled

15 g (½ oz) fresh white breadcrumbs

1 tablespoon sunflower oil

salt and freshly ground black pepper

1. Cook the potatoes in lightly salted, boiling water for 12–15 minutes, until tender. Cook the broccoli in lightly salted, boiling water for 5 minutes. Drain the potatoes and broccoli thoroughly.
2. Meanwhile, melt the margarine in a small saucepan and stir in the flour and mustard powder. Cook, stirring, for 30 seconds. Gradually add the milk and cook, stirring, until you have a smooth, thickened sauce. Reduce the heat to very low and stir the cheese into the sauce. Simmer very gently for 5 minutes, stirring from time to time. Season to taste.
3. Mix the potatoes and broccoli with the cheese sauce, and spoon the mixture into a flameproof dish. Mix together the breadcrumbs and oil, and scatter over the top. Grill under a medium heat for 3–5 minutes until the topping is golden and crispy.

tip: *Blue cheese can be quite salty, so you may not need to add extra salt to this recipe – check the seasoning first.*

Roasted root cobbler

22½ Points per recipe | Takes 25 minutes to prepare, 50 minutes to cook

(v) *Serves 4. Calories per serving 335. Freeze ✓*

225 g (8 oz) carrots, cut into chunks

350 g (12 oz) swede, diced

350 g (12 oz) parsnips, diced

450 g (1 lb) leeks, sliced

150 ml (5 fl oz) vegetable stock

low fat cooking spray

295 g (10 oz) canned low fat condensed
    vegetable soup

For the cobbler:

150 g (5½ oz) self raising white flour plus
    2 teaspoons for rolling

2 tablespoons chopped fresh parsley
    and chives

40 g (1½ oz) polyunsaturated margarine

4 tablespoons low fat plain yogurt

1 tablespoon skimmed milk

a pinch of salt and freshly ground black pepper

1. Preheat the oven to Gas Mark 5/190°C/fan oven 170°C. Mix together the carrots, swede, parsnips and leeks and arrange them in a non stick roasting tin. Pour in the stock and spray the vegetables with low fat cooking spray. Roast in the oven for 25 minutes.

2. Mix the canned soup with the vegetables and spoon the mixture into an ovenproof dish.

3. For the cobbler, sift the flour and stir in the herbs and seasoning. Rub in the margarine with your fingertips until the mixture resembles fine breadcrumbs. Add the yogurt and enough cold water to make a soft dough.

4. Roll out the dough on a lightly floured surface to a thickness of about 1 cm (½ inch) and stamp out rounds with an 7½ cm (3 inch) cutter. Arrange them around the edge of the dish and brush with the milk.

5. Bake for 20–25 minutes until the cobbler topping is risen and golden.

Luxury cauliflower cheese

12½ Points per recipe | Takes 35 minutes

(v) *Serves 4. Calories per servng 220. Freeze ✓*

225 g (8 oz) leeks, sliced

175 g (6 oz) carrots, diced

450 g (1 lb) cauliflower, broken into florets

100 g (3½ oz) frozen peas

300 ml (10 fl oz) skimmed milk

200 g (7 oz) low fat soft cheese

25 g (1 oz) cornflour

25 g (1 oz) half fat Cheddar cheese, grated

15 g (½ oz) fresh wholemeal breadcrumbs

2 teaspoons olive oil

salt and freshly ground black pepper

1. Cook the leeks, carrots and cauliflower in a large saucepan of lightly salted, boiling water for 5 minutes. Add the peas to the pan and cook for a further 5 minutes. Drain well.

2. Meanwhile, gently heat the milk and low fat soft cheese together, whisking until smooth. Mix the cornflour with a little cold water to make a thin paste. When the milk and cheese mixture is almost boiling, add the cornflour paste and cook, stirring, until you have a thick and smooth sauce. Season to taste.

3. Transfer the drained vegetables to a flameproof dish and pour over the sauce. Mix together the grated cheese, breadcrumbs and olive oil, and sprinkle over the top. Grill under a medium heat for 2–3 minutes until the topping is bubbling and golden. Serve at once.

Eggy bread and tomato sandwich

4½ Points per recipe | Takes 15 minutes

(v) *Serves 1. Calories per serving 305. Freeze ✗*

1 egg

4 tablespoons skimmed milk

2 thin slices white bread

1 teaspoon olive oil

1 tomato, sliced

5 basil leaves

salt and freshly ground black pepper

1. Beat together the egg, milk and seasoning and pour into a shallow bowl. Soak the bread slices in the mixture for 5 minutes until they absorb all the liquid.

2. Heat the oil in a large non stick frying pan and add the soaked bread. Cook over a medium heat for 2–3 minutes each side, until the slices are crisp and golden.

3. Arrange the tomato slices on one slice of the cooked bread. Scatter the basil leaves over the tomatoes and lightly press the other slice of bread on top. Transfer the sandwich to a serving plate and slice in half.

Meatless roast with parsley sauce

23½ Points per recipe | Takes 30 minutes to prepare, 1 hour to cook

(v) *Serves 4. Calories per serving 320. Freeze ✓ (roast only)*

Even if you're not a meat eater, you can still enjoy a delicious Sunday roast.

For the roast:

1 tablespoon sunflower oil

1 onion, chopped finely

1 garlic clove, crushed

350 g (12 oz) vegetarian mince

1 tablespoon soy sauce

175 g (6 oz) carrots, grated

1 teaspoon dried mixed herbs

225 g (8 oz) canned baked beans in tomato
   sauce

50 g (1¾ oz) fresh breadcrumbs

1 egg, beaten

salt and freshly ground black pepper

For the sauce:

425 ml (15 fl oz) skimmed milk

25 g (1 oz) polyunsaturated margarine

25 g (1 oz) cornflour

4 tablespoons chopped fresh parsley

salt and freshly ground black pepper

1. Preheat the oven to Gas Mark 4/180°C/fan oven 160°C. Line a 900 g (2 lb) loaf tin with baking parchment.

2. Heat the oil in a frying pan and add the onion, garlic and mince. Stir fry for 5 minutes.

3. Stir in the soy sauce, carrots, herbs and baked beans, and cook for a further 2 minutes.

4. Transfer everything to a large mixing bowl and add the breadcrumbs, beaten egg and seasoning. Use a potato masher to mash all the ingredients together. Spoon the mixture into the prepared tin, levelling it with the back of a spoon, and bake in the oven for 1 hour.

5. To make the sauce, heat the milk until just boiling. Melt the margarine in a medium saucepan, and then remove it from the heat and stir in the cornflour to make a paste. Pour the hot milk over the paste and whisk well. Return the mixture to the heat and cook, stirring, until you have a smooth, thickened sauce. Stir in the chopped parsley and season to taste.

6. Carefully remove the cooked loaf from the tin and peel away the lining paper. Cut it into thick slices and drizzle with a little of the parsley sauce.

tip: *Keep parsley in the freezer; rub it between your hands while it is still frozen and it will be ready to use.*

Veggie cheeseburgers

23 Points per recipe | Takes 30 minutes to prepare, 20 minutes to cook

(V) *Serves 4. Calories per serving 335. Freeze ✓ (burgers only)*

Once you've tried these delicious burgers, you'll never go back to shop bought versions again!

175 g (6 oz) carrots, diced finely	½ teaspoon celery salt
2 teaspoons olive oil	1 tablespoon tomato purée
1 small onion, chopped finely	low fat cooking spray
1 garlic clove, crushed	salt and freshly ground black pepper
100 g (3½ oz) mushrooms, diced	To serve:
425 g (15 oz) canned kidney beans, rinsed and drained	4 burger buns, split
50 g (1¾ oz) fresh wholemeal breadcrumbs	4 reduced fat cheese slices
1 egg, beaten	2 gherkins, sliced
	1 tomato, sliced

1. In a small saucepan, cook the carrots in lightly salted, boiling water for 10 minutes, until tender. Drain thoroughly.
2. Meanwhile, heat the oil in a heavy based non stick frying pan and cook the onion, garlic and mushrooms for 5 minutes until softened. Transfer them to a food processor with the cooked carrots, kidney beans, breadcrumbs, egg, celery salt, tomato purée and black pepper. Blend until the ingredients are evenly combined, but not too smooth.
3. Transfer the mixture to a clean work surface and, using your hands, divide the mixture into four and shape into round flat burgers.
4. Preheat the oven to Gas Mark 6/200°C/fan oven 180°C. Line a baking tray with non stick baking parchment and arrange the burgers on it. Spray each burger with a little low fat cooking spray and bake for 20 minutes.
5. Serve each burger in a split burger bun topped with a cheese slice, gherkins and tomato slices.

try this: *To spice up your burger, add a teaspoon of chilli powder before blending.*

Mediterranean macaroni cheese

21 Points per recipe | Takes 20 minutes to prepare, 20 minutes to cook

(V) *Serves 4. Calories per serving 360. Freeze ✓*

Adding basil, olives and sliced tomatoes makes the world of difference to this popular dish.

425 ml (15 fl oz) skimmed milk	225 g (8 oz) quick cook macaroni
25 g (1 oz) cornflour	50 g (1¾ oz) stoned black olives, halved
1 teaspoon English mustard	2 tablespoons torn fresh basil
100 g (3½ oz) half fat Red Leicester cheese, grated	2 beefsteak tomatoes, sliced
	salt and freshly ground black pepper

1. Reserve 3 tablespoons of milk and heat the rest, until just boiling. In a bowl, mix the cornflour to a paste with the reserved milk. Pour the hot milk into the cornflour paste and stir well. Return the mixture to a clean pan and cook, stirring, until the sauce thickens. Add the mustard and cheese, and stir until the cheese melts. Season to taste.
2. Cook the macaroni in lightly salted, boiling water for about 5 minutes according to the packet instructions. Drain the macaroni well and mix it into the cheese sauce along with the halved olives and basil.
3. Preheat the oven to Gas Mark 5/190°C/fan oven 170°C. Spoon the macaroni mixture into an ovenproof dish and arrange the tomato slices on top. Season with black pepper. Bake in the oven for 20 minutes until bubbling. Serve hot.

Spinach and soft cheese roulade

12½ Points per recipe | **Takes 35 minutes + 30 minutes cooling time**

Ⓥ *Serves 6. Calories per serving 165. Freeze* ✗

Roulades have a similar mixture to soufflés and will puff up in the oven; as it cools the roulade will shrink again, but this is quite normal.

200 g (7 oz) baby spinach leaves	3 eggs, separated
a pinch of ground nutmeg	125 g (4½ oz) low fat soft cheese with
25 g (1 oz) polyunsaturated margarine	garlic and herbs
25 g (1 oz) plain white flour	salt and freshly ground black pepper
200 ml (7 fl oz) skimmed milk	

1. Place the spinach in a medium saucepan with the nutmeg and 2 tablespoons of water. Cover and cook for 2–3 minutes until the spinach has wilted. Drain, squeeze out any excess water and chop the spinach finely.

2. Melt the margarine in a medium saucepan and stir in the flour. Gradually add the milk and cook, whisking until you have a thick, smooth sauce. Stir in the chopped spinach and seasoning, and then whisk in the egg yolks.

3. Preheat the oven to Gas Mark 5/190°C/fan oven 170°C. Line a 23 cm × 28 cm (9 inch × 11 inch) Swiss roll tin with non stick baking parchment.

4. Whisk the egg whites until they form soft peaks. Fold them into the spinach mixture and then turn it all into the prepared tin, and bake for 12 minutes.

5. Turn the roulade out on to a clean sheet of non stick baking parchment and peel away the parchment lining the base. Roll up the roulade like a Swiss roll, using the clean sheet of baking parchment to guide it along. Allow it to cool for 30 minutes.

6. Mash the soft cheese to soften it slightly. Carefully unroll the roulade and spread it with the soft cheese, and then re-roll. Serve cut into slices.

try this: *If you aren't keen on spinach, try using watercress instead. You will only need 150 g (5½ oz) watercress, with the tough stalks removed. The Points will remain the same.*

Summer lemon spaghetti

11 Points per recipe | **Takes 20 minutes**

Ⓥ Ⓥg *Serves 2. Calories per serving 385. Freeze* ✓

A simple, light and refreshing dish with a subtle hint of lemon.

175 g (6 oz) spaghetti	finely grated zest of 1 lemon
225 g (8 oz) frozen broad beans	1 tablespoon fresh lemon juice
low fat cooking spray	2 tablespoons chopped fresh flat leaf parsley
1 garlic clove, crushed	salt and freshly ground black pepper

1. Cook the spaghetti in lightly salted, boiling water for about 8–10 minutes, until tender.

2. Meanwhile, pour boiling water over the frozen broad beans, leave to stand for 5 minutes and then drain. Now remove the beans from their skins.

3. Spray a frying pan with low fat cooking spray. Add the garlic and cook for 30 seconds. Add the lemon zest, lemon juice, broad beans and seasoning and stir fry for 2–3 minutes.

4. Drain the spaghetti and mix it into the pan with the parsley. Serve warm.

Lentil curry

9 Points per recipe | **Takes 20 minutes to prepare, 40 minutes to cook**

V **Vg** *Serves 2. Calories per serving 405. Freeze ✓*

You can save valuable Points by making your own curries at home, as those from Indian takeaways can be very high in Points.

---

low fat cooking spray

1 small onion, sliced

1 garlic clove, crushed

1 small red pepper, de-seeded and diced

175 g (6 oz) potatoes, peeled and diced

175 g (6 oz) carrots, diced finely

125 g (4½ oz) dried, split red lentils

2 tablespoons curry powder

450 ml (16 fl oz) vegetable stock

50 ml (2 fl oz) 88% fat free coconut milk

salt and freshly ground black pepper

2 tablespoons chopped fresh coriander,
   to serve

---

1. Spray a large saucepan with low fat cooking spray and add the onion, garlic, red pepper, potatoes, carrots, lentils and curry powder. Cook, stirring, for 2–3 minutes until all the ingredients are coated with the curry powder.

2. Stir in the stock, seasoning and coconut milk, and bring to the boil. Reduce the heat, cover and simmer for 40 minutes, stirring occasionally to prevent sticking. At the end of the cooking time, the lentils should have absorbed most of the liquid and become soft and fluffy in texture.

3. Spoon the curry into a warmed serving dish and scatter with coriander.

tip: *This is even tastier when left overnight and reheated the next day as the flavours really develop.*

Sesame tofu stir fry

5 Points per recipe | **Takes 25 minutes + 1 hour marinating**

V **Vg** *Serves 2. Calories per serving 315. Freeze ✓*

Whether you are a vegetarian or not, you'll love this tasty stir fry – the longer you marinate the tofu, the better the flavour will be.

---

200 g (7 oz) firm tofu

1 garlic clove, crushed

5 cm (2 inch) piece of root ginger, peeled
   and grated

2 tablespoons Teriyaki sauce

2 tablespoons tomato ketchup

1 tablespoon sherry

1 teaspoon sesame oil

1 tablespoon sesame seeds

low fat cooking spray

175 g (6 oz) carrots, cut into matchsticks

100 g (3½ oz) sugar snap peas, halved
   diagonally

100 g (3½ oz) baby sweetcorn, halved

1 red pepper, de-seeded and sliced

100 g (3½ oz) fresh beansprouts

---

1. Place the tofu in a shallow non-metallic dish. Mix together the garlic, ginger, Teriyaki sauce, tomato ketchup, sherry, sesame oil and sesame seeds and pour this over the tofu. Cover and leave to marinate for up to 1 hour.

2. Spray a large non stick frying pan or wok with low fat cooking spray. Drain the tofu, reserving the marinade, and add it to the pan. Stir fry for 5 minutes over a high heat.

3. Add the carrots, sugar snap peas, baby sweetcorn and red pepper to the pan and stir fry for a further 5 minutes.

4. Add the reserved marinade and beansprouts and cook for a further 2–3 minutes, until the beansprouts have softened and the juices are bubbling. Serve hot.

try this: *Look out for smoked tofu to use instead of plain, it adds a little extra flavour.*

Quorn fajitas

22 Points per recipe | Takes 25 minutes

V *Serves 4. Calories per serving 400. Freeze ✗*

2 tablespoons tomato ketchup	225 g (8 oz) courgettes, sliced
2 tablespoons dark soy sauce	2 red onions, cut into thin wedges
2 garlic cloves, crushed	1 red pepper, de-seeded and sliced
1 teaspoon chilli flakes	8 flour tortillas
3 x 100 g (3½ oz) Quorn fillets, cut into long strips	4 tablespoons low fat natural yogurt
	2 tablespoons chopped fresh coriander
low fat cooking spray	½ Iceberg lettuce, shredded, to garnish

1. In a bowl, mix the tomato ketchup, soy sauce, garlic and chilli flakes. Add the Quorn and mix well.
2. Spray a griddle pan with the low fat cooking spray and heat it until it just starts smoking. Add the Quorn strips, courgettes, onions and pepper to the pan. Cook them for 5–6 minutes over a high heat, until everything is piping hot and beginning to char around the edges. Preheat the oven to Gas Mark 7/220°C/fan oven 200°C.
3. Wrap the tortillas in foil and heat them in the oven for 5 minutes.
4. Divide the filling between the eight tortillas, drizzle over a little yogurt, scatter on the coriander and roll them up tightly. Serve the fajitas with a garnish of shredded Iceberg lettuce, allowing two per serving.

tip: *The tortillas can also be warmed in the microwave set on High. Depending on the power of your microwave, they will take roughly 30 seconds each – but don't wrap them in foil.*

Cheese and onion flan

26 Points per recipe | Takes 35 minutes to prepare, 20 minutes to cook

V *Serves 4. Calories per serving 395. Freeze ✓*

For the pastry:	3 onions, sliced thinly
150 g (5½ oz) plain white flour plus 2 teaspoons for rolling	1 garlic clove, crushed
	3 tablespoons vegetable stock
a pinch of salt	2 eggs
75 g (2¾ oz) polyunsaturated margarine	150 ml (5 fl oz) skimmed milk
For the filling:	125 g (4½ oz) low fat soft cheese
1 teaspoon olive oil	salt and freshly ground black pepper

1. Preheat the oven to Gas Mark 6/200°C/fan oven 180°C. To make the pastry, sift the flour and salt in a mixing bowl. Rub in the margarine using your fingertips until the mixture resembles fine breadcrumbs. Mix in enough cold water to make a soft dough.
2. Roll out the pastry on a lightly floured surface and use it to line a 20 cm (8 inch) loose bottomed flan tin. Line the base of the pastry with non stick baking parchment and fill the flan up with baking beans. Bake in the oven for 10 minutes, and then remove the beans and paper and bake 'blind' for a further 10 minutes.
3. Meanwhile, heat the oil in a medium saucepan and add the onions, garlic and stock. Cover and cook gently for 15 minutes until the onions have softened. Remove the cover, turn up the heat and cook until the liquid evaporates.
4. Whisk together the eggs, milk, soft cheese and seasoning. Arrange the cooked onion mixture over the base of the pastry case. Carefully pour the egg mixture over the top and return the flan to the oven for 20 minutes, until the filling is set and golden. Cut into wedges to serve.

Herb omelette

4½ Points per recipe | Takes 15 minutes

(V) *Serves 1. Calories per serving 280. Freeze ✗*

2 large eggs

2 tablespoons chopped fresh mixed herbs
  (e.g. chives, parsley, coriander and basil)

2 tablespoons skimmed milk

1 teaspoon sunflower oil

1 tomato, de-seeded and chopped finely

salt and freshly ground black pepper

1. Beat the eggs with the herbs, milk and seasoning.

2. Heat the oil in a small non stick frying pan. Pour in the egg mixture and cook over a medium to low heat. As the egg sets, drag the edges into the centre of the pan, so the uncooked mixture runs to the outer edge.

3. When all the egg has just about set, scatter the chopped tomato over the top. Using a spatula, flip one half of the omelette over the other. Transfer to a warmed plate and eat at once.

tip: *The smaller the frying pan the deeper your omelette will be. An 18 cm (7 inch) pan is ideal.*

Scrambled egg with mushrooms

5½ Points per recipe | Takes 15 minutes

(V) *Serves 1. Calories per serving 260. Freeze ✗*

low fat cooking spray

150 g (5½ oz) open cup mushrooms, sliced

2 eggs

2 tablespoons half fat crème fraîche

1 teaspoon finely chopped fresh chives

salt and freshly ground black pepper

1. Spray a small frying pan with low fat cooking spray and fry the mushrooms until softened. If the mushrooms ooze a lot of liquid as they cook, drain this off.

2. Beat together the eggs, crème fraîche, chives and seasoning, and pour this mixture over the mushrooms. Cook, stirring, until the eggs start to scramble. Serve immediately.

Pesto, quorn and pepper kebabs

6 Points per recipe | Takes 20 minutes

(V) *Serves 2. Calories per serving 280. Freeze ✓*

225 g (8 oz) Quorn pieces

2 tablespoons pesto

1 red pepper, de-seeded and cut into squares

1 green pepper, de-seeded and cut into squares

1 yellow pepper, de-seeded and cut into
  squares

2 small red onions, cut into thick wedges

8 bay leaves

1. Place the Quorn pieces in a bowl with the pesto and mix well.

2. Thread the pesto coated Quorn pieces on to four skewers alternating with squares of pepper, red onion wedges and bay leaves.

3. Grill for 8–10 minutes, turning frequently, until the vegetables begin to char around the edges. Serve two kebabs per person.

Tomato and chive soufflé omelette

3½ Points per recipe | **Takes 20 minutes**

(V) *Serves 1. Calories per serving 260. Freeze ✗*

Omelettes are a quick and easy option, especially when cooking for one. Serve with Zero Point vegetables for a substantial meal.

2 eggs, separated	1 large tomato, de-seeded and chopped finely
3 tablespoons skimmed milk	1 teaspoon finely chopped fresh chives
1 teaspoon sunflower oil	salt and freshly ground black pepper

1. Beat together the egg yolks, milk and seasoning.
2. Whisk the egg whites until they form soft peaks and then fold them into the yolk and milk mixture.
3. Heat the oil in a heavy based non stick 20 cm (8 inch) frying pan. Carefully pour the egg mixture into the pan and cook over a low to medium heat, until the egg begins to set. This will take 6–8 minutes.
4. Scatter the tomatoes and chives over the omelette and then use a spatula to carefully flip one side of the omelette over the other. Cook for a further 2 minutes. Transfer the omelette to a warmed plate and eat at once.

Plain and simple gnocchi with tomatoes

5½ Points per recipe | **Takes 20 minutes**

(V) (Vg) *Serves 2. Calories per serving 245. Freeze ✓*

It's filling and tasty, yet so simple to make.

400 g can of chopped tomatoes	2 tablespoons tomato purée
2 tablespoons medium dry white wine	225 g (8 oz) fresh gnocchi
1 garlic clove, crushed	2 tablespoons torn fresh basil
1 teaspoon caster sugar	salt and freshly ground black pepper

1. Place the tomatoes in a medium saucepan with the wine, garlic, sugar, tomato purée and seasoning. Bring to the boil, reduce the heat and simmer for 15 minutes.
2. Meanwhile, bring a large saucepan of lightly salted water to the boil and cook the gnocchi. They cook very quickly in about 2–3 minutes. When they rise to the top of the water, they are done.
3. Drain the gnocchi well and add them to the tomato sauce. Scatter over the basil and serve.

try this: *De-seeded, chopped red and green peppers can also be added to the sauce for more colour and texture.*

Thai green pumpkin curry

7 Points per recipe | Takes 25 minutes to prepare, 25 minutes to cook

V **Vg** Serves 4. Calories per serving 110. Freeze ✓

This recipe follows the authentic Thai method for making curries. The stock, paste and coconut milk are boiled first, and the other ingredients are then added. This means you don't need to add oil, making a delicious yet low Point curry.

600 ml (20 fl oz) vegetable stock

2 tablespoons Thai green curry paste

25 g (1 oz) creamed coconut, crumbled

6 shallots, halved

2 garlic cloves, sliced thinly

450 g (1 lb) pumpkin or butternut squash, peeled and cubed

150 g (5½ oz) fine green beans, sliced

225 g (8 oz) cherry tomatoes, halved

3 tablespoons chopped fresh coriander, to serve

1. Pour the stock into a large saucepan and add the curry paste and creamed coconut. Bring to the boil, stirring, until the coconut dissolves.

2. Boil the sauce rapidly for 5 minutes, and then add the shallots, garlic, pumpkin or butternut squash and green beans. Cook over a medium heat, so it keeps bubbling, for 20 minutes or until the pumpkin or squash is tender.

3. Add the tomatoes and cook for a further 5 minutes. Sprinkle over the coriander just before serving.

tip: *Thai curries are generally quite liquid and are served with Jasmine rice which has a sticky texture; this helps to soak up the wonderful sauce. Add 3 Points for 4 tablespoons of cooked rice.*

goes well with...

half a pint of lager for an extra 1 Point.

Potato parcels

5 Points per recipe | Takes 20 minutes to prepare, 30 minutes to cook

V **Vg** *Serves 4. Calories per serving 90. Freeze* ✓

This is an interesting way to cook potatoes as it keeps all their flavour in and there's also no pan to clear up afterwards!

450 g (1 lb) small new potatoes, scrubbed
   and sliced

1 red onion, sliced

1 garlic clove, sliced very thinly

4 sprigs of fresh thyme

low fat cooking spray

125 ml (4 fl oz) vegetable stock

salt and freshly ground black pepper

1. Preheat the oven to Gas Mark 5/190°C/fan oven 170°C.

2. Lay four sheets of non stick baking parchment, about 30 cm (12 inches) square, on a flat work surface.

3. Divide the potato and onion slices between the parchment sheets. Top each potato and onion pile with a little garlic, a sprig of thyme and seasoning. Spray each mound with a little low fat cooking spray.

4. Gather together the edges of each paper sheet, to enclose the potatoes, but do not seal them up yet. Pour a little stock into each parcel and then fold the paper over a few times to completely enclose the mixture.

5. Place the parcels on a baking sheet and bake for 30 minutes.

tip: *Make sure you wrap up the baking parchment tightly as the steam that forms in the parcels cooks the potatoes and be very careful as you open each parcel as steam will escape and may burn you.*

Button mushroom provençal

7½ Points per recipe | Takes 10 minutes to prepare, 15 minutes to cook

V **Vg** *Serves 2. Calories per serving 395. Freeze* ✗

Serve this as a tasty snack or light lunch with a mixed leaf salad.

1 teaspoon olive oil

350 g (12 oz) button mushrooms

2 shallots, chopped finely

1 garlic clove, crushed

4 tablespoons medium white wine

225 g can of chopped tomatoes

½ teaspoon caster sugar

2 x 75 g (2¾ oz) pieces of French bread

2 tablespoons chopped fresh parsley

salt and freshly ground black pepper

1. Heat the olive oil in a frying pan and add the mushrooms, shallots and garlic. Stir fry for 2 minutes and then pour in the wine, tomatoes and sugar.

2. Bring to the boil and then cook over a fairly high heat for 10 minutes, until the sauce reduces a little.

3. Meanwhile, toast the French bread pieces until they are lightly golden. Once the mushroom sauce has reduced, stir in the parsley and season to taste.

4. Arrange the toasts on two serving plates and spoon the mushrooms on top.

tip: *For the best results, choose firm small mushrooms. Any large mushrooms should be halved.*

try this: *For a more interesting version of this dish try using a selection of mushrooms, such as chestnut, shiitake, oyster, or any of the wild mushrooms that are available in the supermarkets.*

fish...
and shellfish

7 POINTS

Pizza marinara

27½ Points per recipe | **Takes 30 minutes to prepare, 20 minutes to cook + 10 minutes cooling**
Serves 4. Calories per serving 390. Freeze ✓

300 g (10½ oz) pizza base mix

1 teaspoon plain white flour, for rolling

low fat cooking spray

1 small onion, sliced

1 garlic clove, crushed

225 g can of chopped tomatoes

2 tablespoons tomato purée

1 teaspoon caster sugar

½ teaspoon dried oregano

50 g (1¾ oz) cooked prawns, peeled

125 g (4½ oz) canned tuna in brine, drained
and flaked

1 green pepper, de-seeded and cut into
thin rings

25 g (1 oz) stoned black olives, sliced

100 g (3½ oz) mozzarella light, sliced thinly

freshly ground black pepper

1. Preheat the oven to Gas Mark 6/200°C/fan oven 180°C. Make up the pizza base mix according to the packet instructions, using warm water. Knead the dough for 5 minutes. Dust a work surface with the flour and roll out the dough to a 30 cm (12 inch) circle to form the pizza base. Place it on a non stick baking tray.

2. Cover the baking tray with a damp tea towel while you prepare the topping.

3. Heat a small saucepan and spray it with low fat cooking spray. Add the onion and garlic to the pan and cook, stirring occasionally, over a medium to low heat, until the onion has softened but not browned.

4. Stir in the chopped tomatoes, tomato purée, sugar and oregano, and simmer for 10 minutes. Allow the mixture to cool for 10 minutes and then spread it over the pizza base to within 1 cm (½ inch) of the edge.

5. Scatter the prawns, tuna, pepper rings and sliced olives over the pizza and finally top with the mozzarella cheese slices. Season with black pepper.

6. Bake the pizza for 20 minutes and then cut it into quarters to serve.

try this: *Try other zero Point vegetables on top of the pizza, such as ribbons of courgettes, sliced mushrooms or fresh tomatoes.*

Smoked trout with fried potatoes

3½ Points per recipe | Takes 30 minutes

Serves 1. Calories per serving 260. Freeze ✗

This is a lovely fish version of the favourite American hash dish – it's true comfort food!

---

175 g (6 oz) potatoes, peeled and diced

low fat cooking spray

75 g (2¾ oz) peppered, smoked trout fillets,
    skinned and flaked

2 spring onions, sliced

75 g (2¾ oz) cherry tomatoes, halved

½ teaspoon freshly grated lemon zest

1 teaspoon fresh lemon juice

a pinch of salt

---

1. Bring a small saucepan of lightly salted water to the boil and cook the potatoes for 5 minutes, until just tender. Drain well and then use kitchen paper to absorb any extra moisture.

2. Heat a small non stick frying pan and spray it with low fat cooking spray. Add the potatoes and stir fry them for 5 minutes, until they begin to brown slightly – keep them moving in the pan to prevent them sticking.

3. Add the flaked trout fillets, spring onions, cherry tomatoes, lemon zest, lemon juice, and salt to taste. Mix well and heat it all through for 2–3 minutes.

4. Pile the trout and potato mixture on to a warmed plate to serve.

Seafood paella

21½ Points per recipe | Takes 40 minutes

Serves 4. Calories per serving 415. Freeze ✓

Bring back memories of summer holidays and recreate your own special version of this popular Spanish dish.

¼ teaspoon turmeric

2 tablespoons boiling water

low fat cooking spray

1 onion, chopped

1 garlic clove, crushed

300 g (10½ oz) easy cook long grain
    white rice

1 red pepper, de-seeded and diced

1 green pepper, de-seeded and diced

600 ml (20 fl oz) fish stock

225 g (8 oz) skinless cod fillet, cubed

150 g (5½ oz) cooked prawns, peeled

225 g (8 oz) mussels in their shells,
    cleaned and scrubbed

2 tomatoes, de-seeded and diced

salt and freshly ground black pepper

1 tablespoon chopped fresh flat leaf parsley,
    to serve

---

1. In a small cup, mix the turmeric with the boiling water.

2. Spray a large non stick saucepan with low fat cooking spray. Add the onion, garlic, rice and peppers. Cook, stirring, for 2 minutes. Add the stock and turmeric liquid and bring to the boil. Reduce the heat, cover and simmer for 10 minutes.

3. Remove the cover and add the cod, prawns and mussels in their shells – discarding any open mussels that do not close when tapped. Cover the pan and cook for a further 5 minutes; by which time the fish should be cooked and the mussel shells should have opened. Discard any mussel shells that have not opened.

4. Add the tomatoes, season and sprinkle with parsley before serving.

try this: *To save time, you could use a packet of seafood cocktail that normally contains shelled mussels, prawns, squid rings and shreds of crabsticks, remembering to adjust the Points accordingly.*

    For the real authentic flavour of paella, use a few saffron strands instead of turmeric and follow the same instructions.

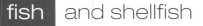

fish and shellfish

Smoked fish risotto

17½ Points per recipe | Takes 45 minutes

Serves 4. Points per serving 330. Freeze ✓

This tasty supper dish combines creamy rice with smoked haddock and a hint of spice.

---

low fat cooking spray

1 onion, chopped

225 g (8 oz) risotto rice

1 tablespoon medium curry powder

700 ml (1¼ pints) fish stock

100 g (3½ oz) frozen peas

350 g (12 oz) skinless, smoked haddock
    fillets, cubed

2 tablespoons chopped fresh parsley

2 tablespoons low fat plain fromage frais

freshly ground black pepper

---

1. Spray a large frying pan with low fat cooking spray and add the onion. Cook over a low heat until the onion is softened but not browned.

2. Stir in the rice and curry powder and cook for 1 minute. Add 150 ml (5 fl oz) of the stock and cook until the liquid has been absorbed; this will take about 5 minutes. Add three more amounts of stock in the same way, only adding more when the liquid has been absorbed by the rice.

3. Add the final 150 ml (5 fl oz) of stock with the peas and haddock. Cover the pan and cook for 5 minutes until the fish is cooked, the stock is absorbed and the rice is tender.

4. Fold the parsley and fromage frais into the risotto and season with black pepper. Serve.

tip: *Take care when stirring in the fromage frais and parsley as you don't want to break up the fish too much.*

Baked thai salmon

9 Points per recipe | Takes 15 minutes to prepare, 20 minutes to cook

Serves 2. Calories per serving 320. Freeze ✓

The fresh, vibrant flavours of ginger and lime complement the salmon superbly in this delightful dish.

---

2 x 150 g (5½ oz) skinless salmon fillets

100 g (3½ oz) carrots, cut into very thin strips

100 g (3½ oz) leeks, cut into very thin strips

1 teaspoon finely grated lime zest

1 tablespoon Thai fish sauce

1 garlic clove, sliced very thinly

2 cm (¾ inch) piece of fresh root ginger,
    peeled and grated

2 tablespoons 88% fat free coconut milk

1 tablespoon chopped fresh coriander

---

1. Preheat the oven to Gas Mark 5/190°C/fan oven 170°C.

2. Line a roasting tin with non stick baking parchment. Lay the salmon fillets in the tin.

3. Mix together the carrots, leeks, lime zest, fish sauce, garlic, ginger and coconut milk in a small bowl. Spoon this mixture on top of each salmon fillet, and then sprinkle over the chopped fresh coriander. Bake for 20 minutes.

4. Use a fish slice to transfer each salmon fillet to a warmed plate.

tip: *For this dish, shred the vegetables as thinly as you can for a really professional touch.*

try this: *This topping works equally well on cod or haddock fillets. Adjust the Points accordingly.*

Mackerel macaroni supper

29 Points per recipe | Takes 30 minutes

Serves 4. Calories per serving 585. Freeze ✓

A quick, simple and satisfying supper dish for those days when you don't have a lot of time to spend in the kitchen.

225 g (8 oz) quick cook macaroni

low fat cooking spray

225 g (8 oz) courgettes, diced

400 g can of chopped tomatoes with garlic

300 g (10½ oz) peppered mackerel, skinned
    and flaked

4 spring onions, sliced

100 g (3½ oz) half fat mature Cheddar
    cheese, grated

salt

1. Bring a large saucepan of lightly salted water to the boil and cook the macaroni for about 5 minutes until tender.
2. Meanwhile heat a large non stick frying pan and spray it with low fat cooking spray. Add the courgettes to the pan and cook them for 2–3 minutes to soften them.
3. Add the cooked macaroni, chopped tomatoes, mackerel and spring onions to the pan, stir well and heat through for 5 minutes.
4. Spoon the mixture into a flameproof dish and sprinkle the cheese over the top. Grill under a medium heat for 5 minutes and serve at once.

Cod with orange sauce

11 Points per recipe | Takes 30 minutes

Serves 4. Calories per serving 190. Freeze ✗

The orange sauce in this recipe complements the cod perfectly as the citrus draws out its flavour.

4 x 150 g (5½ oz) cod fillets, skinned

300 ml (10 fl oz) fish stock

thinly pared zest of 1 orange

¼ teaspoon turmeric

2 tablespoons light soy sauce

½ teaspoon dried sage or 1 teaspoon
    fresh chopped sage

2 tablespoons cornflour

2 tablespoons orange liqueur (e.g. Cointreau)

salt and freshly ground black pepper

225 g (8 oz) fine green beans, to serve

1. Place the cod in a frying pan and pour over the stock. Add the orange zest and turmeric, and bring to the boil. Reduce the heat, cover and simmer for 10 minutes, until the fish is cooked through.
2. Remove the fish from the pan and set aside.
3. Add the soy sauce, sage and black pepper to the pan and bring to the boil. Allow the mixture to bubble for 2 minutes.
4. Mix together the cornflour with the orange liqueur and stir this into the pan. Cook, stirring, until the sauce thickens. Return the cod to the pan and heat through for 2 minutes.
5. Meanwhile, cook the beans in boiling, salted water for 5 minutes, and then drain them. Serve the fish on a bed of fine green beans with the sauce spooned over.

try this: *If you prefer not to use liqueur, substitute it with orange juice. The Points will remain the same.*

Cod and pancetta kebabs

14½ Points per recipe | Takes 20 minutes

Serves 4. Calories per serving 200. Freeze ✗

Pancetta is an Italian cured ham that is generally sold sliced very thinly, a little like Parma ham.

450 g (1 lb) skinless, boneless cod fillet	225 g (8 oz) cherry tomatoes
100 g (3½ oz) pancetta	8 bay leaves
350 g (12 oz) shallots	low fat cooking spray

1. Cut the cod into bite sized cubes and wrap a piece of pancetta around each cube.

2. Thread the wrapped fish pieces on to four skewers, alternating them with the shallots, cherry tomatoes and bay leaves.

3. Spray each kebab with low fat cooking spray and grill for 10 minutes, under a medium heat, turning frequently until the fish is cooked through.

tips: *The shallots will remain quite crisp. If you prefer them softer, cook them in a pan of boiling water for 5 minutes before threading them on to the skewers.*

If you can't get hold of any pancetta, thin rashers of streaky bacon make a good alternative. The Points will be 3½ per serving.

Summer barbecue

Make the most of summer with these fabulous low Point dishes.

Zero Point carrot salad *page 28*, 1 serving....................0 Points

Potato salad *page 31*, 1 serving..................................3 Points

Cod and pancetta kebabs *above*, 1 serving.................3½ Points
(pictured right)

Summer berry pudding *page 171*, 1 serving..................2 Points

Total Points for meal ....**8½ Points**

Salmon and spinach parcels

25 Points per recipe | Takes 20 minutes to prepare, 20 minutes to cook

Serves 4. Calories per serving 385. Freeze ✗

If you are having friends around for dinner try this easy recipe. The crispy parcels look very impressive and taste delicious.

---

4 x 100 g (3½ oz) salmon fillets

150 g (5½ oz) baby spinach leaves

4 teaspoons low fat mayonnaise

8 sheets of filo pastry

25 g (1 oz) polyunsaturated margarine, melted

1 teaspoon poppy seeds

salt and freshly ground black pepper

---

1. Preheat the oven to Gas Mark 5/190°C/fan oven 170°C. Rinse the salmon and pat it dry with kitchen paper.
2. Place the spinach in a medium saucepan with 2 tablespoons of water and seasoning. Cover and simmer for 2–3 minutes, until the spinach wilts. Drain well.
3. Place a quarter of the spinach over each salmon fillet and top each with a teaspoon of mayonnaise.
4. Sandwich two sheets of filo pastry together with a light brushing of the melted margarine. Place a salmon fillet in the centre and wrap the pastry around it like a parcel. Repeat this process with the rest of the pastry and the remaining three salmon fillets. Brush the tops of the parcels with any remaining margarine and sprinkle with poppy seeds.
5. Bake for 20 minutes, until the pastry is crisp and golden.

tip: *Because filo pastry is so thin it dries out very quickly and becomes brittle. To prevent this, keep the sheets of pastry covered with a damp tea towel until you are ready to use them.*

Peppered trout with watercress sauce

12 Points per recipe | Takes 25 minutes

Serves 2. Calories per serving 290. Freeze ✓

---

4 x 75 g (2¾ oz) skinless trout fillets

4 teaspoons fresh lemon juice

a pinch of salt

freshly ground mixed pepper

For the sauce:

150 g (5½ oz) watercress

100 ml (3½ fl oz) vegetable stock

1 teaspoon horseradish sauce

3 tablespoons half fat crème fraîche

1 tablespoon cornflour

2 tablespoons skimmed milk

---

1. Line a baking sheet with non stick baking parchment. Rinse the trout fillets and pat them dry with kitchen paper. Place them on the baking sheet and season well with freshly ground mixed pepper.
2. Mix together the lemon juice and salt, and drizzle this over the fish. Grill the fish under a medium heat for 5–6 minutes until it is cooked through.
3. Meanwhile, place the watercress in a medium saucepan with the stock. Simmer for 2 minutes until the watercress wilts. Transfer it to a food processor or liquidiser and blend until smooth. Return the sauce to a clean saucepan and stir in the horseradish sauce and crème fraîche.
4. Mix the cornflour with the milk to make a thin paste and stir this into the pan. Cook, stirring, until the sauce thickens a little.
5. Transfer two cooked trout fillets per person to warmed serving plates and drizzle over the watercress sauce.

tip: *Hand held blenders are very good and inexpensive, perfect for blending sauces and soups – what's more they are so much easier to wash too!*

Cod and parsley fish cakes

15½ Points per recipe | Takes 40 minutes to prepare, 20 minutes to cook

Serves 4. Calories per serving 235. Freeze ✓

These delicious home made fish cakes served warm with a crisp green zero Point salad garnish make a filling lunch.

450 g (1 lb) potatoes, diced	2 tablespoons plain white flour
300 g (10½ oz) skinless cod fillet	1 egg, beaten
3 lemon slices	75 g (2¾ oz) natural dried white breadcrumbs
2 tablespoons chopped fresh parsley	low fat cooking spray
1 teaspoon horseradish sauce	salt and freshly ground black pepper

1. Cook the potatoes in lightly salted, boiling water for 12–15 minutes until tender. Drain and mash thoroughly.
2. Place the cod with the lemon slices in a large frying pan and cover with water. Bring to the boil and then reduce the heat and simmer for 5 minutes, until the fish is cooked. Drain well and flake the fish.
3. Preheat the oven to Gas Mark 5/190°C/fan oven 170°C. Add the fish, parsley, horseradish sauce and seasoning to the mashed potatoes, and mix together thoroughly.
4. Divide the mixture into eight and then shape into small, round, flat cakes with your hands.
5. Line a baking tray with non stick baking parchment. Dust the cakes with the flour and then dip them in the beaten egg. Coat the fish cakes lightly in the breadcrumbs and then spray them with low fat cooking spray. Place them on the baking tray.
6. Bake the fish cakes in the oven for 20 minutes until the breadcrumbs have turned golden and crisp.

tip: *You can buy natural dried breadcrumbs in supermarkets. They have a better flavour than the bright yellow variety.*

Smoked haddock fish balls

10 Points per recipe | Takes 40 minutes

Serves 4. Calories per serving 195. Freeze ✓

Wholegrain mustard goes particularly well with smoked fish; it certainly livens up these tasty fish balls.

350 g (12 oz) skinless, smoked haddock	15 g packet of low fat ready salted crisps, crushed
4 tablespoons skimmed milk	low fat cooking spray
450 g (1 lb) cooked potatoes, mashed with no fat	salt and freshly ground black pepper
2 teaspoons wholegrain mustard	

1. Preheat the oven to Gas Mark 6/200°C/fan oven 180°C.
2. Place the fish in a large saucepan with the milk and 4 tablespoons of water, and bring to the boil. Cover and simmer for 5 minutes until the fish flakes easily. Drain, reserving the liquid, and carefully flake the fish.
3. Place the mashed potatoes in a large mixing bowl. Add the flaked fish, 3 tablespoons of the reserved cooking liquid, mustard and seasoning. Mix it all together thoroughly and then shape the mixture into eight small balls with your hands.
4. Line a baking tray with non stick baking parchment. Roll the balls in the crushed crisps and arrange them on the baking tray. Spray them with low fat cooking spray and bake in the oven for 15 minutes. Serve hot.

tip: *Try making this delicious dip to serve with the haddock balls: mix 4 tablespoons low fat plain fromage frais with 1 tomato, de-seeded, skinned and diced finely and 1 teaspoon finely chopped fresh chives. Season and chill the dip until you need it. Remember to add ½ a Point per serving.*

Warm teriyaki tuna

8 Points per recipe | Takes 35 minutes

Serves 2. Calories per serving 390. Freeze ✗

275 g (9½ oz) fresh tuna steaks, cut into thin strips

3 tablespoons Teriyaki sauce

1 garlic clove, crushed

1 tablespoon tomato purée

200 g (7 oz) baby new potatoes, scrubbed and halved

125 g (4½ oz) mange tout peas

low fat cooking spray

2 oranges, peeled and segmented

4 tablespoons orange juice

salt

1. Arrange the tuna strips in a shallow dish. Mix together the Teriyaki sauce, garlic and tomato purée and pour it over the tuna. Toss the tuna in the marinade and set aside. Leave it to marinate while you prepare the potatoes.

2. Cook the potatoes in lightly salted, boiling water for 10 minutes until tender. Add the mange tout peas to the pan and cook for a further 2 minutes. Drain well.

3. Spray a frying pan with low fat cooking spray. Drain the tuna strips, reserving the marinade, and add them to the pan. Cook the tuna over a high heat for 2 minutes, and then add the potatoes, mange tout peas and orange segments. Carefully stir fry for a further 2 minutes, taking care not to break up the tuna.

4. Divide the stir fry mixture between two serving plates. Add the marinade to the pan with the orange juice. Allow the liquid to bubble and then drizzle this sauce over the tuna mix. Serve at once.

Haddock florentine

15½ Points per recipe | Takes 40 minutes

Serves 4. Calories per serving 245. Freeze ✗

This is the perfect dish for Saturday brunch. Serve it as soon as the egg is cooked.

300 g (10½ oz) baby spinach leaves

a pinch of ground nutmeg

450 g (1 lb) skinless, smoked haddock fillets

4 tablespoons skimmed milk

4 tablespoons half fat crème fraîche

2 tomatoes, sliced

1 teaspoon distilled malt vinegar

4 eggs

salt and freshly ground black pepper

1. Place the spinach in a medium size saucepan with 2 tablespoons of water and the nutmeg. Cover and cook for 2 minutes until the spinach wilts. Drain it thoroughly.

2. Place the haddock in a frying pan with the milk and 4 tablespoons of water. Bring to the boil. Reduce the heat, cover and poach the fish for 8 minutes until the fish flakes easily. Drain the fish and flake it into large chunks. Carefully mix the fish with the crème fraîche and the spinach. Season to taste.

3. Divide the fish and spinach mixture between four individual gratin dishes. Top with the sliced tomatoes. Season to taste. Place the dishes under a preheated grill for 2 minutes and then keep warm.

4. Bring a large saucepan of water to the boil and add the vinegar. Add the eggs one at a time and poach them gently for about 7 minutes until the whites are firm but the yolks are a little runny. Drain the poached eggs on kitchen paper to remove any excess liquid. Top each gratin dish with an egg and serve at once.

tip: *When poaching eggs, use the biggest saucepan you have, half fill it with water and add vinegar. Using the handle of a wooden spoon, swirl the boiling water and drop in the egg. The swirling movement binds the white together.*

Roasted tomato cod with parsley mash

20 Points per recipe | Takes 35 minutes

Serves 4. Calories per serving 300. Freeze ✓
Tasty comfort food, perfect for a wintry evening.

For the mash:

700 g (1 lb 9 oz) potatoes, peeled and diced

3 tablespoons low fat plain fromage frais

2 tablespoons chopped fresh parsley

salt and freshly ground black pepper

For the fish:

4 x 150 g (5½ oz) skinless cod fillets

2 tablespoons sun dried tomato purée

1 fresh tomato, de-seeded and chopped finely

25 g (1 oz) stoned black olives, chopped finely

salt and freshly ground black pepper

1. Preheat the oven to Gas Mark 5/190°C/fan oven 170°C. Cook the potatoes in lightly salted, boiling water for 15 minutes, until tender. Drain thoroughly and mash them with the fromage frais, parsley and seasoning. Cover and keep warm.

2. Meanwhile, place the cod fillets in a non stick roasting tin. Mix together the sun dried tomato purée, chopped tomato and olives. Spread this mixture over the top of each cod fillet, and bake for 15 minutes.

3. Spoon a little of the mash on to four serving plates and top with a cooked cod fillet. Season with a little salt and black pepper and serve.

try this: *Flavour your mash with other ingredients, such as crushed garlic, a teaspoon of wholegrain mustard or toasted cumin seeds. Adding parsley or any fresh herb also gives it that little extra flavour.*

Parmesan lemon sole

11½ Points per recipe | Takes 20 minutes to prepare, 15 minutes to cook

Serves 4. Calories per serving 170. Freeze ✓
Lemon sole is a delicate fish with a soft texture. When you skin each fillet, you'll probably find that you end up with two small fillets – this is fine. Serve this dish with freshly cooked zero Point vegetables such as fine green beans and oven roasted cherry tomatoes.

4 x 100 g (3½ oz) lemon sole fillets, skinned

2 tablespoons plain white flour

50 g (1¾ oz) fresh white breadcrumbs

25 g (1 oz) Parmesan cheese, grated

1 egg, beaten

low fat cooking spray

salt and freshly ground black pepper

1. Preheat the oven to Gas Mark 5/190°C/fan oven 170°C

2. Rinse the sole fillets and pat them dry with kitchen paper. Mix the flour with a little seasoning and dust this lightly over each fillet.

3. Combine the breadcrumbs and Parmesan cheese in a shallow dish. Dip each floured fillet in the beaten egg and then into the breadcrumb mixture.

4. Spray the coated fillets with low fat cooking spray and then lay them on a non stick baking sheet. Bake for 15 minutes until the fish fillets are cooked and the breadcrumb coating is crunchy and golden.

Baked cod with anchovies and garlic

18 Points per recipe | Takes 30 minutes

Serves 4. Calories per serving 280. Freeze ✗

Cod loins are now widely available from supermarkets. They are the best part of the fillet which has been skinned and trimmed into a neat, rounded piece of fish.

4 x 175 g (6 oz) cod loins	**450 g (1 lb) baby new potatoes, scrubbed**
50 g (1¾ oz) canned anchovy fillets, drained	**25 g (1 oz) low fat spread**
1 garlic clove, crushed	**1 tablespoon finely chopped fresh chives**
2 tablespoons tomato purée	**salt and freshly ground black pepper**

1. Preheat the oven to Gas Mark 5/190°C/fan oven 170°C. Place the cod on a non stick baking tray.
2. Pat the anchovy fillets with kitchen paper to remove any excess oil. In a small bowl, mash the anchovies with the garlic and tomato purée to make a thick paste. Spread the anchovy paste over each cod loin. Bake the cod in the oven for 20 minutes.
3. Meanwhile, cook the potatoes in lightly salted, boiling water for 15 minutes, until tender. Drain them and, using a potato masher, break up the potatoes by lightly crushing them. Mix in the low fat spread and chives, and season with plenty of freshly ground black pepper.
4. Divide the crushed potatoes between four warmed serving plates and top with a cod loin.

tip: *Anchovies are very salty, so you shouldn't need to add any extra salt to this dish.*

Classic fish stew

7 Points per recipe | Takes 20 minutes to prepare, 20 minutes to cook

Serves 4. Calories per serving 295. Freeze ✗

Fennel is a bulb shaped vegetable with a texture a little like celery and a subtle aniseed taste; it goes particularly well with the orange flavours in this recipe.

low fat cooking spray	**2 tablespoons tomato purée**
225 g (8 oz) leeks, sliced	**2 sprigs of fresh thyme or 1 teaspoon**
1 fennel bulb, shredded thinly	**dried thyme**
½ teaspoon cayenne pepper	**150 ml (5 fl oz) fish stock**
finely grated zest and juice of 1 orange	**350 g (12 oz) skinless haddock fillets, cubed**
3 tablespoons Pernod	**100 g (3½ oz) cooked prawns, peeled**
400 g can of chopped tomatoes	**salt and freshly ground black pepper**

1. Spray a small saucepan with low fat cooking spray, and add the leeks and fennel. Cover the pan and cook gently for about 5 minutes until the vegetables are tender.
2. Stir in all the ingredients except the haddock and prawns, and bring to the boil. Simmer, uncovered, for 15 minutes.
3. Add the haddock and prawns and cook for a further 5 minutes, until the fish is cooked through and flakes easily. Season to taste.

tip: *Look out for small prawns or cooking prawns in the freezer cabinets of supermarkets, they are less expensive than ordinary prawns and work perfectly well for this recipe.*

Red jungle curry

15½ Points per recipe | Takes 30 minutes

Serves 4. Calories per serving 200. Freeze ✓

In Thailand a jungle curry refers to a curry made without coconut milk. Serve this delicious version with boiled Jasmine rice, but don't forget to add an extra 3 Points for 4 tablespoons of cooked rice.

600 ml (20 fl oz) fish stock	100 g (3½ oz) fine green beans, halved
2 tablespoons red Thai curry paste	350 g (12 oz) salmon fillets, skinned and
1 tablespoon Thai fish sauce	cubed
finely grated zest and juice of 1 lime	225 g (8 oz) cherry tomatoes, halved
2 lemongrass stalks, sliced thinly	3 tablespoons chopped fresh coriander

1. Pour the fish stock into a large saucepan, stir in the curry paste, fish sauce, lime zest and juice and lemongrass. Bring to the boil and allow the mixture to bubble for 5 minutes.

2. Add the green beans and cook for 5 minutes. Stir in the salmon and tomatoes and cook for a further 5 minutes, or until the salmon is cooked and flakes easily.

3. Scatter the coriander over the top and then ladle the curry into bowls to serve.

tip: *Most major supermarkets now sell fresh lemongrass stalks in the fresh herb section. To prepare lemongrass, peel away the outer skin and slice it very thinly. You can also buy ready prepared lemongrass.*

Prawn pasta bake

25 Points per recipe | Takes 25 minutes to prepare, 20 minutes to cook

Serves 4. Calories per serving 460. Freeze ✗

This makes a quick and easy evening meal, especially if you have some prawns in the freezer; ensure they are defrosted.

350 g (12 oz) pasta shells	225 g (8 oz) cooked prawns, peeled
400 g can of chopped tomatoes	150 ml (5 fl oz) 0% fat Greek style plain
225 g (8 oz) courgettes, diced	yogurt
100 g (3½ oz) mushrooms, sliced	25 g (1 oz) Parmesan cheese, grated
1 garlic clove, crushed	coarsely
2 tablespoons torn fresh basil	salt and freshly ground black pepper

1. Bring a large saucepan of lightly salted water to the boil and cook the pasta according to the packet instructions or for about 10 minutes, until tender. Drain well.

2. Meanwhile, preheat the oven to Gas Mark 5/190°C/fan oven 170°C. Place the chopped tomatoes, courgettes, mushrooms, garlic and basil in a large saucepan and heat gently for a few minutes.

3. Mix the cooked pasta into the tomato sauce mixture. Add the prawns and seasoning, and mix well. Spoon it all into an ovenproof dish and drizzle over the yogurt. Sprinkle the Parmesan cheese on the surface and bake for 20 minutes.

tip: *Keep a lump of Parmesan cheese in the freezer, it's much tastier than the ready grated variety and you'll always have some to hand. It will also grate from frozen.*

Crab and asparagus fettucine

11 Points per recipe | **Takes 10 minutes**

Serves 2. Calories per serving 415. Freeze ✗

---

200 g can of white crab meat, drained

½ teaspoon chilli flakes

1 teaspoon fresh lemon juice

175 g (6 oz) fettucine

150 g (5½ oz) asparagus tips

salt and freshly ground black pepper

---

1. Place the drained crab meat, chilli flakes and lemon juice in a bowl and mix them together thoroughly.
2. Bring a large saucepan of lightly salted water to the boil and cook the pasta for about 10 minutes, or until tender. Add the asparagus to the pan for the last 2 minutes of the cooking time.
3. Drain the fettucine and asparagus well, reserving 3 tablespoons of the cooking water. Return it to a clean pan with the reserved water and the crab mixture. Heat through gently and season to taste. Serve at once.

try this: *Try using canned tuna in brine, drained and flaked. The Points per serving will then be 5½.*

Fluffy tuna jackets

8 Points per recipe | **Takes 15 minutes to prepare, 1¼ hours to cook**

Serves 2. Calories per serving 270. Freeze ✓

---

2 x 225 g (8 oz) baking potatoes

100 g (3½ oz) canned tuna in brine, drained and flaked

50 g (1¾ oz) low fat soft cheese

50 g (1¾ oz) canned or frozen sweetcorn

1 egg white

salt and freshly ground black pepper

---

1. Preheat the oven to Gas Mark 6/200°C/fan oven 180°C.
2. Prick the potatoes all over. Bake them for 1 hour until they are tender. Slice them in half and, using a small teaspoon, carefully scoop out the flesh into a small bowl. Reserve the potato skins.
3. Add the drained flaked tuna, low fat soft cheese, sweetcorn and seasoning to the potato flesh and stir well.
4. Whip the egg white until it forms stiff peaks and fold it into the potato and tuna mixture. Spoon the mixture into the potato shells and return them to the oven for 15 minutes to heat through.

Prawn and mushroom pilaff

16 Points per recipe | **Takes 30 minutes**

Serves 4. Calories per serving 320. Freeze ✓

---

225 g (8 oz) mixed wild and white rice

15 g (½ oz) polyunsaturated margarine

350 g (12 oz) chestnut mushrooms, sliced

1 garlic clove, crushed

finely grated zest and juice of 1 orange

1 tablespoon chopped fresh tarragon

225 g (8 oz) fresh raw tiger prawns, peeled

salt and freshly ground black pepper

---

1. Cook the rice as directed on the packet for about 25 minutes, and drain well.
2. Melt the margarine in a frying pan. Add the mushrooms and garlic. Stir fry until the mushrooms are soft.
3. Add the orange zest and juice, tarragon and seasoning, and allow the sauce to bubble for 2 minutes.
4. Mix in the cooked rice and tiger prawns, and cook, stirring, for a further 5 minutes, until the prawns turn pink.

Haddock and sweetcorn pie

20 Points per recipe | **Takes 25 minutes to prepare, 25 minutes to cook**

Serves 4. Calories per serving 360. Freeze ✓

If you prefer, make four individual pies in small dishes rather than one large pie. You could then freeze any you don't require.

---

700 g (1 lb 9 oz) potatoes, peeled and diced

3 tablespoons 0% fat Greek style plain yogurt

25 g (1 oz) polyunsaturated margarine

25 g (1 oz) plain white flour

300 ml (10 fl oz) skimmed milk

2 teaspoons wholegrain mustard

2 tablespoons chopped fresh parsley

200 g (7 oz) broccoli, broken into florets

400 g (14 oz) smoked haddock fillets, skinned and cubed

125 g (4½ oz) canned sweetcorn, drained

salt and freshly ground black pepper

---

1. Cook the potatoes in lightly salted, boiling water for 15 minutes, until tender. Drain well and mash them with the yogurt and a little seasoning.

2. Meanwhile, melt the margarine in a small saucepan, then stir in the flour, and cook for 1 minute. Gradually add the milk and simmer, stirring constantly, until you have a smooth, thickened sauce. Mix in the mustard and parsley.

3. Cook the broccoli florets in a little lightly salted, boiling water for 2 minutes. Drain the broccoli and stir it into the sauce with the smoked haddock and sweetcorn.

4. Preheat the oven to Gas Mark 5/190°C/fan oven 170°C. Spoon the fish mixture into an ovenproof dish. Spread the mashed potatoes on top and bake the pie in the oven for 20–25 minutes, until piping hot and bubbling.

tip: *When cooking potatoes to make mash, remember the smaller you dice them, the quicker they will cook.*

goes well with...

a 175 ml (6 fl oz) glass of white wine for an extra 2 Points.

Quick sardine penne

10 Points per recipe | **Takes 20 minutes**

Serves 2. Calories per serving 330. Freeze ✗

125 g (4½ oz) penne	1 tablespoon fresh lemon juice
150 g (5½ oz) canned sardines in tomato sauce	2 tablespoons torn fresh basil
	salt and freshly ground black pepper

1. Cook the penne in lightly salted, boiling water for about 10 minutes until tender. Drain well.
2. Place the sardines and their tomato sauce in a bowl. Mash with a fork. Stir in the lemon juice, basil and seasoning.
3. Return the pasta to a large saucepan. Add the sardine mixture. Heat through for 2–3 minutes and serve hot.

try this: *Try this dish with pilchards instead of sardines. The Points will then be 5½ per serving.*

Sweet and sour fish curry

3½ Points per recipe | **Takes 45 minutes**

Serves 2. Calories per serving 260. Freeze ✓

This is quite a mild curry with the pineapple adding sweetness to the sauce.

low fat cooking spray	1 tablespoon fresh lemon juice
1 small red onion, cubed	100 g (3½ oz) baby sweetcorn, halved
75 g (2¾ oz) carrots, diced finely	100 g (3½ oz) canned pineapple chunks in natural juice, drained
1 garlic clove, crushed	
1 tablespoon korma curry powder	275 g (9½ oz) skinless haddock fillet, cubed
150 g (5½ oz) courgettes, diced	2 tablespoons chopped fresh coriander, to serve
400 g can of chopped tomatoes	
150 ml (5 fl oz) fish stock	

1. Heat a heavy based large saucepan and spray it with low fat cooking spray. Add the onion, carrots, garlic and curry powder with 2 tablespoons of water, and cook, stirring, over a low heat for 5 minutes, until the vegetables have softened.
2. Add the courgettes, chopped tomatoes, fish stock and lemon juice to the pan, and bring to the boil. Reduce the heat and simmer, uncovered, for 15 minutes.
3. Mix in the baby sweetcorn, pineapple and haddock cubes, stir well and cook for a further 10 minutes.
4. Sprinkle with coriander just before serving.

Prawn and tuna pancakes

13½ Points per recipe | Takes 35 minutes

Serves 4. Calories per serving 245. Freeze ✓ (see tip)

For the pancakes:

100 g (3½ oz) plain white flour

1 egg

300 ml (10 fl oz) skimmed milk

a pinch of salt

low fat cooking spray

For the filling:

400 g can of chopped tomatoes

½ teaspoon dried oregano

50 g (1¾ oz) low fat soft cheese with garlic and herbs

185 g can of tuna in brine, drained and flaked

125 g (4½ oz) cooked prawns, peeled

4 spring onions, sliced thinly

salt and freshly ground black pepper

1. To prepare the pancakes, sift the flour into a mixing bowl and make a well in the centre. Add the egg and milk with a pinch of salt and whisk to a smooth batter.

2. Spray a non stick 20 cm (8 inch) heavy based frying pan with a little low fat cooking spray and heat. Add 1 large tablespoon of batter to the pan and swirl it so it evenly coats the base of the pan. Cook for 2 minutes, flip the pancake over and cook for a further 2 minutes. Slide it on to a warmed plate and repeat the process with the remaining batter to make eight pancakes. Cover the pancakes with foil and keep them warm.

3. For the filling, place the tomatoes, oregano and low fat soft cheese in a medium saucepan. Heat gently, stirring, until the cheese has melted into the tomatoes and the sauce is piping hot.

4. Add the tuna, prawns and spring onions to the pan and cook for a further 2–3 minutes. Season to taste.

5. To serve, spoon equal amounts of the filling on to each pancake and roll them up. Serve hot.

tip: *Freeze the pancakes and the sauce separately. Wrap the pancakes in a double thickness of foil and spoon the filling into a freezer container. To serve, warm the pancakes in the oven and simmer the filling for 5 minutes.*

Fish pie

14½ Points per recipe | Takes 40 minutes to prepare, 25 minutes to cook

Serves 4. Calories per serving 270. Freeze ✓

Fish pie is a real favourite with everyone; the basil in the mash makes this one extra tasty.

700 g (1 lb 9 oz) potatoes, peeled and diced

3 tablespoons skimmed milk

2 tablespoons torn fresh basil

350 g (12 oz) cod fillets, skinned and cubed

150 g (5½ oz) cooked fresh prawns, peeled

400 g can of chopped tomatoes with basil

4 celery sticks, sliced thinly

1 garlic clove, crushed

125 g (4½ oz) mushrooms, sliced

salt and freshly ground black pepper

1. Cook the potatoes in lightly salted, boiling water for 15 minutes, until tender. Drain and mash them thoroughly with the milk and basil.

2. Meanwhile, preheat the oven to Gas Mark 5/190°C/fan oven 170°C.

3. Mix together the cod cubes, prawns, chopped tomatoes, celery, garlic, mushrooms and seasoning. Spoon the mixture into an ovenproof dish.

4. Spread the potatoes over the top of the fish mixture and bake for 25 minutes. Serve hot.

try this: *For a really fluffy mashed potato topping, fold a whisked egg white into the potatoes before topping the fish mixture. The Points will remain the same.*

Tuna and broccoli quiche

26 Points per recipe | Takes 35 minutes to prepare, 50 minutes to cook + 20 minutes chilling

Serves 4. Calories per serving 395. Freeze ✓

For the pastry:

150 g (5½ oz) plain white flour plus

2 teaspoons for rolling

15 g (½ oz) cornflour

75 g (2¾ oz) polyunsaturated margarine

a pinch of salt

For the filling:

150 g (5½ oz) broccoli florets

185 g can of tuna in brine, drained and flaked

2 eggs

300 ml (10 fl oz) skimmed milk

salt and freshly ground black pepper

1. To make the pastry, sift the flour and cornflour into a mixing bowl. Rub in the margarine, using your fingertips, until the mixture resembles fine breadcrumbs. Add a pinch of salt and enough cold water to make a soft dough.

2. Roll out the pastry on a lightly floured surface and use it to line a 20 cm (8 inch) loose bottomed fluted flan tin. Chill the pastry in the fridge for 20 minutes.

3. Preheat the oven to Gas Mark 6/200°C/fan oven 180°C. Line the pastry case with non stick baking parchment and baking beans, and bake blind for 10 minutes. Remove the paper and the beans, and return the flan tin to the oven for 5 minutes.

4. Meanwhile, cook the broccoli in lightly salted, boiling water for 5 minutes, and then drain it. Arrange the broccoli and the tuna in the partially baked pastry case.

5. Reduce the oven temperature to Gas Mark 4/180°C/fan oven 160°C. Whisk together the eggs and milk with a little seasoning and pour the mixture over the broccoli and tuna. Put the flan on a baking tray and return it to the oven for 45–50 minutes, until the filling has set. Serve warm or cold.

goes well with...

a crisp Zero Point salad.

Fish'n'chips for one

7½ Points per recipe | Takes 40 minutes

Serves 1. Calories per serving 455. Freeze ✓

When you fancy fish and chips but don't want to use too many Points, this recipe will guarantee you satisfaction!

---

175 g (6 oz) potatoes, cut into thin sticks

1 tablespoon sunflower oil

½ teaspoon salt

1 x 175 g (6 oz) cod loin

1 teaspoon plain white flour

1 egg white

25 g (1 oz) fresh white breadcrumbs

low fat cooking spray

lemon wedge, to garnish

---

1. Preheat the oven to Gas Mark 6/200°C/fan oven 180°C.
2. Rinse the potato sticks to remove the excess starch and pat dry with kitchen paper. Place them in a plastic container with a tight fitting lid. Add the oil and sprinkle in the salt. Place the lid on the container and shake thoroughly so all the potatoes get a thin coating of salty oil.
3. Spread the chips out on a non stick baking sheet and bake for 20–25 minutes, until they are golden and crispy.
4. Meanwhile, rinse the cod loin and pat dry with kitchen paper, and then dust it with the flour.
5. Whisk the egg white until it becomes foamy. Dip the fish into the egg white and then coat it in the breadcrumbs. Lightly spray the crumbed fish with low fat cooking spray and then place it on a non stick baking tray.
6. Bake the fish for 15–20 minutes, until it is cooked through and the crumb coating is golden and crunchy.
7. Serve the fish and chips on a warmed serving plate and garnish with a wedge of lemon.

tip: *Preheat the baking tray for 5 minutes before putting the fish on to it, to make the fish crispy underneath.*

Thai style fish cakes

20½ Points per recipe | Takes 25 minutes to prepare, 25 minutes to cook

Serves 4. Calories per serving 370. Freeze ✓

The green curry paste in these fish cakes gives them a sensational flavour.

---

450 g (1 lb) cod fillets, skinned and cubed

2 tablespoons Thai green curry paste

3 tablespoons chopped fresh coriander

1 tablespoon Thai fish sauce

1 egg white, whisked lightly

100 g (3½ oz) fine green beans, chopped finely

low fat cooking spray

275 g (9½ oz) Jasmine or basmati rice

4 spring onions, sliced

1 teaspoon chilli sauce

salt

---

1. Place the cod, Thai curry paste, coriander, fish sauce and egg white in a food processor and pulse blend until evenly combined.
2. Transfer the mixture to a mixing bowl and fold in the green beans. Before shaping the fish cakes, wet your hands under cold running water to prevent the mixture sticking to you. Shape eight round flat cakes. Spray a non stick frying pan with low fat cooking spray and cook the fish cakes for 5 minutes on each side, until golden.
3. Meanwhile, cook the rice according to the packet instructions in lightly salted, boiling water for 10–12 minutes, until tender. Drain thoroughly.
4. Mix the spring onions and chilli sauce with the rice. Divide the rice mixture between four serving plates and top with two fish cakes.

tip: *Make sure you remove any small bones from the fish – the easiest way to do this is with tweezers.*

chicken...
and turkey

Turkey and ham pie

31½ Points per recipe | **Takes 40 minutes to prepare, 30 minutes to cook**

Serves 4. Calories per serving 445. Freeze ✓

2 teaspoons sunflower oil

350 g (12 oz) turkey breast, diced

125 g (4½ oz) wafer thin ham, cut into
   thin strips

350 g (12 oz) leeks, sliced

175 g (6 oz) mushrooms, sliced

150 ml (5 fl oz) chicken stock

25 g (1 oz) polyunsaturated margarine

25 g (1 oz) plain white flour

300 ml (10 fl oz) skimmed milk plus
   1 tablespoon for glazing

1 teaspoon dried mixed herbs

150 g (5½ oz) shortcrust pastry, defrosted
   if frozen

salt and freshly ground black pepper

1. Heat the sunflower oil in a non stick frying pan and cook the diced turkey for 5 minutes to seal it. Add the ham, leeks and mushrooms, pour over the stock and bring it to the boil. Cover and cook for 15 minutes.

2. Meanwhile, preheat the oven to Gas Mark 5/190°C/fan oven 170°C.

3. Heat the margarine in a small saucepan and stir in the flour. Cook for 1 minute and then gradually pour in the milk. Cook, stirring, until the sauce thickens and then stir in the herbs and seasoning. Pour the sauce over the turkey mixture and stir well.

4. Spoon the mixture into a deep ovenproof dish with a lip. Roll out the pastry to form a lid for the pie. Dampen the lip of the dish with a little of the reserved milk. Place the rolled out pastry over the filling and press it down well around the rim of the dish trimming off any excess. Use a fork to stamp a pattern around the edge, using the pastry trimmings to decorate. Brush the top with the remaining milk and bake for 30 minutes, until the pastry is golden and crisp.

tip: *This recipe is an excellent way to use up any leftover cooked turkey. Just add it along with the ham, leek and mushrooms, and then follow the recipe as it is.*

Chicken parcels with vegetable ribbons

7 Points per recipe | Takes 20 minutes to prepare, 30 minutes to cook

Serves 4. Calories per serving 185. Freeze ✗

When you invite guests around for dinner it doesn't mean you have to stray from the Programme. There are a huge variety of impressive dishes you can conjure up that look and taste great – here is one of them!

1 teaspoon paprika	4 x 100 g (3½ oz) skinless chicken breasts
1 teaspoon Chinese five spice powder	175 g (6 oz) carrots
½ teaspoon salt	175 g (6 oz) courgettes
1 garlic clove, crushed	4 spring onions, sliced into long, thin strips
2.5 cm (1 inch) piece of root ginger, peeled	4 tablespoons light soy sauce
and cut into very thin strands	1 teaspoon sesame oil

1. Preheat the oven to Gas Mark 5/190°C/fan oven 170°C.

2. Cut a sheet of non stick baking parchment into four 30 cm (12 inch) squares. Lay them out, side by side, on a clean work surface.

3. Mix together the paprika, five spice powder, salt, garlic and ginger. Rub this mixture into the chicken breasts.

4. Place one chicken breast in the centre of each sheet of baking parchment.

5. Using a swivel head potato peeler, peel the carrots and courgettes into thin ribbons. Place the ribbons in a large bowl, followed by the spring onions and soy sauce and mix well.

6. Pile equal amounts of the vegetable ribbons over each chicken breast and drizzle over the sesame oil and any soy sauce left in the bowl. Wrap the parchment up tightly to enclose the chicken and vegetables. Put the chicken parcels in a roasting tin.

7. Bake for 30 minutes. Unwrap the parcels carefully on to warmed serving plates.

tip: *Because of the strong flavours in this recipe, you only need a very simple accompaniment, such as boiled Jasmine rice or baby new potatoes. Add 3 Points for 4 tablespoons of cooked rice and 2 Points per 200 g (7 oz) of boiled potatoes.*

Cajun chicken goujons

20½ Points per recipe | Takes 35 minutes + 20 minutes marinating

Serves 4. Calories per serving 365. Freeze ✓

450 g (1 lb) skinless chicken breasts, cut into strips	2 tablespoons chopped fresh coriander
2 tablespoons Cajun spice mix	225 g (8 oz) easy cook rice
100 ml (3½ fl oz) low fat plain yogurt	75 g (2¾ oz) canned sweetcorn, drained
finely grated zest of 2 limes	salt

1. Place the chicken in a shallow dish. Mix together the Cajun spice mix, yogurt, zest of 1 lime and the coriander. Spoon this over the chicken. Stir well to coat all the strips. Cover and leave to marinate for 20 minutes.

2. Meanwhile, cook the rice in lightly salted, boiling water for 12 minutes until tender. Drain and mix the rice with the remaining lime zest and the sweetcorn. Cover and keep warm.

3. Grill the chicken for 12–15 minutes, turning frequently, until the chicken is cooked through and slightly browned.

4. Spoon the rice on to four individual serving plates and pile the Cajun chicken on top.

Chicken burgers

11½ Points per recipe | Takes 25 minutes

Serves 2. Calories per serving 330. Freeze ✓ (burger only)

For the burgers:

225 g (8 oz) chicken mince

½ small red onion, chopped finely

1 egg, beaten

25 g (1 oz) fresh wholemeal breadcrumbs

1 teaspoon dried mixed herbs

To serve:

2 burger buns

1 tablespoon low fat mayonnaise

1 Little Gem lettuce, shredded

1 tomato, sliced

1. Place all the burger ingredients in a bowl and mix well. Shape two round flat burgers with your hands.
2. Cook the burgers under a hot grill for 5 minutes on each side.
3. Split each burger bun in half and toast them lightly. Spread one half of each with a little low fat mayonnaise and top with lettuce and tomato. Place a burger and the remaining half bun on top of each. Serve at once.

Chicken and vegetable curry

10½ Points per recipe | Takes 25 minutes to prepare, 1 hour to cook

Serves 4. Calories per serving 265. Freeze ✓

This tastes even better the day after, as the flavours will have had time to develop.

low fat cooking spray

350 g (12 oz) skinless chicken breasts, diced

1 onion, chopped

225 g (8 oz) potatoes, peeled and diced

225 g (8 oz) carrots, sliced

1 aubergine, diced

2 garlic cloves, crushed

**2 fresh green chillies, de-seeded and
    chopped finely**

3 tablespoons medium curry powder

50 g (1¾ oz) dried, split red lentils

400 g can of chopped tomatoes

300 ml (10 fl oz) chicken stock

salt and freshly ground black pepper

**2 tablespoons chopped fresh coriander,
    to serve**

1. Heat a large non stick frying pan and spray it with low fat cooking spray. Add the chicken and stir fry over a high heat until it is evenly browned. Add the onion, potatoes, carrots, aubergine, garlic, chillies and curry powder to the pan. Stir well so that all the ingredients get an even coating of the curry powder. Cook for 2 minutes.
2. Stir in the lentils, chopped tomatoes, stock and seasoning, and bring to the boil. Reduce the heat, cover and simmer for 1 hour, stirring from time to time.
3. Spoon into four warmed bowls and scatter with chopped fresh coriander to serve.

Turkey and cranberry burgers

22 Points per recipe | **Takes 25 minutes**

Serves 4. Calories per serving 288. Freeze ✓

As we all know turkey and cranberries are the perfect combination, so there is no reason why we should reserve it just for Christmas.

450 g (1 lb) turkey mince	salt and freshly ground black pepper
2 tablespoons cranberry sauce	To serve:
50 g (1¾ oz) fresh wholemeal breadcrumbs	4 burger buns
1 egg	¼ Iceberg lettuce, shredded
4 spring onions, sliced thinly	4 tomato slices

1. Place the mince in a large mixing bowl and add the cranberry sauce, breadcrumbs, egg, spring onions and seasoning.

2. Using clean hands, combine the mixture together thoroughly.

3. Divide the mixture into four and shape into burgers with your hands. Grill the burgers under a medium heat for 15 minutes, turning half way through the cooking time.

4. To serve, split the burger buns in half and place a cooked burger in each with a little shredded lettuce and a tomato slice.

tip: *Burgers are always a welcome speedy snack, but home made ones are so much more tasty than the shop bought variety and have fewer Points too. Why not make a double batch and freeze them individually, then you'll always have some fast food available!*

Bonfire night

This low Point menu will give you something warming and filling to look forward to after the fireworks.

Zero Point casserole *page 72*, I serving...............0 Points

Turkey and cranberry burgers *above*, I serving .....5½ Points (*pictured left*)

Oaty crumbles *page 196*, I serving..................1½ Points

Total Points per meal............................7 Points

Chicken and shallot kebabs

5½ Points per recipe | **Takes 20 minutes to prepare, 15 minutes to cook**

Serves 2. Calories per serving 195. Freeze ✓

These tasty kebabs, with a hint of exotic Greek flavours, are delicious served hot or cold.

225 g (8 oz) skinless chicken breasts, cubed	**2 teaspoons olive oil**
1 teaspoon clear honey	**8 shallots**
2 tablespoons chopped fresh mint	**4 bay leaves**
½ teaspoon dried oregano	**freshly ground black pepper**
finely grated zest and juice of ½ lemon	To serve:
¼ teaspoon salt	**fresh salad leaves**
1 garlic clove, chopped very finely	**lemon wedges**

1. Place the chicken in a dish with the honey, mint, oregano, lemon zest and juice, salt, garlic, olive oil and black pepper. Mix together well.

2. Thread the chicken pieces and shallots on to four skewers – allow two shallots per skewer, and thread a bay leaf half way through.

3. Grill the kebabs under a medium heat for 10–15 minutes, turning frequently, until the chicken is golden and cooked through.

4. Serve two kebabs per person on a bed of mixed salad leaves, garnished with a lemon wedge.

tip: *If you prefer the shallots with a softer texture, place them in a small saucepan of water and bring to the boil. Reduce the heat, cover and simmer for 5 minutes before threading them on the skewers.*

Sage and orange turkey escalopes

12½ Points per recipe | **Takes 15 minutes to prepare, 30 minutes to cook**

Serves 4. Calories per serving 235. Freeze ✓

This dish has a delicious sauce which is ideal with mashed potatoes, but remember to add the extra Points.

4 x 150 g (5½ oz) turkey escalopes	**½ teaspoon dried sage**
low fat cooking spray	**150 ml (5 fl oz) chicken stock**
1 red onion, cut into thin wedges	**1 orange, sliced**
300 ml (10 fl oz) fresh orange juice	**1 tablespoon cornflour**
1 tablespoon wholegrain mustard	**salt and freshly ground black pepper**

1. Season the turkey escalopes on both sides with a little salt and black pepper.

2. Heat a large non stick frying pan and spray it with low fat cooking spray. Add the turkey to the pan and cook for 2–3 minutes on each side, until lightly browned. Add the onion wedges to the pan and cook for a further 2 minutes.

3. Add the orange juice, the mustard, sage and chicken stock. Arrange the orange slices over the top of the escalopes and bring the liquid to the boil. Reduce the heat, cover the pan and cook for 20 minutes.

4. Mix the cornflour to a thin paste with a little cold water and stir this into the pan. Cook, stirring, until the sauce thickens a little. Transfer the escalopes to warmed plates and spoon the sauce over them to serve.

tips: *If you have difficulty finding turkey escalopes, try using turkey breast steaks instead, but hammer them flat with the flat end of a rolling pin. The Points will remain the same.*

Use orange juice from freshly squeezed oranges if you can for this recipe.

Chicken and mushroom stroganoff

11½ Points per recipe | Takes 25 minutes to prepare, 25 minutes to cook

Serves 4. Calories per serving 170. Freeze ✓

Stroganoff is traditionally made with beef, but this lighter version is every bit as delicious. It's great served with zero Point fine green beans or mange tout peas to add a burst of colour to the dish.

low fat cooking spray	1 tablespoon Worcestershire sauce
1 onion, sliced	2 tablespoons brandy
1 garlic clove, crushed	1 chicken stock cube
350 g (12 oz) skinless chicken breasts, cut into thin strips	300 ml (10 fl oz) boiling water
	100 g (3½ oz) half fat crème fraîche
225 g (8 oz) button mushrooms, sliced	2 tablespoons chopped fresh parsley
1 teaspoon paprika	salt and freshly ground black pepper

1. Heat a large non stick frying pan. Spray it with low fat cooking spray and add the onion and garlic. Reduce the heat and cook gently for 5 minutes until the onion has softened, but not browned. Add the chicken to the pan and stir fry for 5 minutes until it is sealed on all sides.

2. Add the mushrooms, paprika, Worcestershire sauce and brandy, and cook, stirring, for 2 minutes. Crumble the stock cube into the pan and add the boiling water. Bring to the boil, and then reduce the heat and simmer, uncovered, for 20 minutes, stirring from time to time.

3. Add the crème fraîche, seasoning and parsley. Stir well and heat through gently for 2 minutes – don't allow it to boil and bubble as the sauce may separate.

tip: If you omit the brandy you will save ½ a Point per portion.

Caribbean chicken

24 Points per recipe | Takes 30 minutes to prepare, 35 minutes to cook

Serves 4. Calories per serving 355. Freeze ✗

2 teaspoons sunflower oil	350 g (12 oz) sweet potatoes, peeled and diced
400 g (14 oz) skinless chicken thighs	4 celery sticks, sliced
1 teaspoon chilli flakes	300 ml (10 fl oz) chicken stock
1 teaspoon Caribbean seasoning	400 g can of chopped tomatoes
1 onion, chopped	100 ml (3½ fl oz) red wine
2 garlic cloves, crushed	300 g (10½ oz) canned red kidney beans, drained and rinsed
1 red pepper, de-seeded and diced	
1 green pepper, de-seeded and diced	2 tablespoons chopped fresh coriander

1. Heat the sunflower oil in a large non stick saucepan and add the chicken thighs. Cook them for 5 minutes, turning them halfway through, and then sprinkle in the chilli flakes and Caribbean seasoning.

2. Add the onion, garlic, peppers, sweet potatoes and celery to the pan, and mix well. Add the chicken stock, tomatoes and wine, and bring to the boil. Reduce the heat, cover and simmer for 30 minutes.

3. Add the kidney beans and cook for a further 5 minutes. Scatter with chopped fresh coriander just before serving.

tip: Caribbean seasoning is now widely available; you can even find supermarket own brand varieties.

try this: Add a few extra chilli flakes to this dish if you like your food extra spicy.

Chicken and thyme risotto

24 Points per recipe | **Takes 30 minutes to prepare, 20 minutes to cook**

Serves 4. Calories per serving 430. Freeze ✓

To achieve a traditional, creamy risotto serve it straight away; if you leave it sitting around too long the rice becomes a little stodgy.

1 tablespoon olive oil	275 g (9½ oz) risotto rice
1 onion, chopped	100 ml (3½ fl oz) dry white wine
1 garlic clove, crushed	850 ml (1½ pints) chicken stock
125 g (4½ oz) fennel bulb, shredded thinly	2 teaspoons fresh thyme
400 g (14 oz) skinless chicken breasts, diced	salt and freshly ground black pepper

1. Heat the oil in a large heavy based frying pan and add the onion, garlic, fennel and chicken. Stir fry for 5 minutes, until the chicken is sealed on all sides, stir in the rice and cook for 2 minutes.
2. Add the wine and cook until all the liquid has evaporated. Gradually add the stock, a little at a time and cook, stirring, until the rice is tender and the stock has been absorbed. This will take about 20 minutes.
3. Season to taste and sprinkle in the thyme. Serve immediately.

tip: *Fennel is now widely available in supermarkets – it is a bulb shaped vegetable with a texture similar to celery and it has a subtle aniseed flavour.*

try this: *If you find the flavour of fennel too strong, use 4 celery sticks, sliced, instead. The Points will remain the same.*

Blue cheese chicken

17 Points per recipe | **Takes 15 minutes to prepare, 25 minutes to cook + 5 minutes standing**

Serves 4. Calories per serving 225. Freeze ✓

Fit for entertaining, these tasty little bundles are perfect served with a selection of freshly cooked zero Point vegetables for a fantastic feast.

4 x 125 g (4½ oz) skinless chicken breasts	4 slices (25 g/1 oz) wafer thin ham
50 g (1¾ oz) blue cheese (e.g. Stilton), crumbled	1 teaspoon olive oil
	salt and freshly ground black pepper
2 tablespoons low fat mayonnaise	

1. Preheat the oven to Gas Mark 5/190°C/fan oven 170°C. Line a baking tray with non stick baking parchment.
2. Make slits along the length of each chicken breast to form deep pockets. Place the blue cheese in a small bowl with the mayonnaise and seasoning, and mix together thoroughly. Spoon equal amounts of the mixture into each chicken breast pocket.
3. Wrap a slice of wafer thin ham around each chicken breast and secure it with a cocktail stick. Place the wrapped chicken on a baking tray and brush with olive oil. Bake for 25 minutes. Leave the chicken to stand for 5 minutes before slicing in half on the diagonal to serve.

try this: *For a tasty accompaniment, mix 4 tablespoons reduced sugar blackcurrant jam with 2 tablespoons of port and 1 teaspoon of finely grated orange zest. Warm through in a small saucepan and serve a spoonful with each chicken breast, adding ½ a Point per serving.*

Chicken enchiladas

25 Points per recipe | **Takes 25 minutes**

Serves 4. Calories per serving 345. Freeze ✗

These tasty wraps are quick to make and fun to eat.

8 flour tortillas	1 green pepper, de-seeded and sliced
350 g (12 oz) skinless chicken breasts, cut into thin strips	1 red onion, cut into wedges
1 teaspoon chilli sauce	175 g (6 oz) courgettes, cut into thin sticks
low fat cooking spray	2 tablespoons chopped fresh coriander
1 red pepper, de-seeded and sliced	50 g (1¾ oz) half fat Cheddar, grated
	1 lime, cut into wedges

1. Preheat the oven to Gas Mark 6/200°C/fan oven 180°C. Wrap the flour tortillas in foil and heat them in the oven for 10 minutes.

2. Meanwhile, mix the chicken with the chilli sauce. Spray a griddle pan with low fat cooking spray and heat until just smoking.

3. Cook the chicken strips for 2–3 minutes, until they are sealed. Add the peppers, onion and courgettes and cook for a further 5 minutes, until they are lightly charred. Scatter over the coriander.

4. To serve, unwrap the flour tortillas and scatter a little grated cheese over each one. Top with the cooked chicken mixture and a squeeze of juice from a lime wedge. Fold the tortilla into quarters and eat while hot.

try this: (V) *For a vegetarian alternative, use strips of Quorn fillet instead of the chicken. The Points per serving will remain the same.*

tip: *If you don't have a griddle pan, use the heaviest frying pan you have to cook the chicken.*

Roast chicken with lemon, garlic and thyme

24½ Points per recipe | **Takes 20 minutes to prepare, 1 hour 25 minutes to cook**

Serves 4. Calories per serving 375. Freeze ✓

This is the perfect roast for a Sunday lunch or Saturday supper when friends or family pop round.

1.5 kg (3 lb 5 oz) whole chicken	freshly ground black pepper
2 lemons, quartered	For the roasties:
2 heads of garlic, broken into unpeeled cloves	700 g (1 lb 9 oz) potatoes, peeled and diced
a bunch of fresh thyme	1 teaspoon salt
1 teaspoon salt	1 tablespoon olive oil

1. Preheat the oven to Gas Mark 5/190°C/fan oven 170°C. Rinse the chicken well, remembering to remove any giblets. Pat dry with kitchen paper and place it in a non stick roasting tin.

2. Push the lemons, garlic and thyme sprigs into the chest cavity of the chicken.

3. Sprinkle the salt and pepper all over the skin of the chicken, rubbing it in with your fingers. Roast for 1 hour 25 minutes.

4. Meanwhile, place the diced potatoes in a plastic container that has a tightly fitting lid. Add the salt and oil, place the lid on the container and shake well, so that all the pieces of potato get a light covering of salty oil. Arrange the potatoes in a single layer on a non stick baking tray.

5. About 35 minutes towards the end of the chicken's cooking time, place the potatoes in the oven to roast.

6. Serve 150 g (5½ oz) thinly carved slices of chicken per person with a few crispy roasties.

tip: *Two heads of garlic sounds an awful lot, but because the cloves are not peeled they just impart a subtle flavour.*

Slow cooked chicken with mushrooms

20 Points per recipe | Takes 15 minutes to prepare, 1½ hours to cook

Serves 4. Calories per serving 200. Freeze ✓

This recipe has a slightly Mediterranean feel to it. Serve it simply with crusty French bread for a delicious winter warmer. A 5 cm (2 inch) piece of French stick is 1½ Points.

low fat cooking spray	400 g can of chopped tomatoes
1 onion, chopped	1 tablespoon balsamic vinegar
2 garlic cloves, crushed	300 ml (10 fl oz) chicken stock
4 x 75 g (2¾ oz) skinless, boneless chicken thighs	350 g (12 oz) open cup mushrooms
	salt and freshly ground black pepper
4 x 75 g (2¾ oz) chicken drumsticks, skinned	2 tablespoons torn fresh basil, to serve

1. Heat a large, heavy based saucepan and spray it with low fat cooking spray. Add the onion, garlic and chicken portions. Cook for 5 minutes, turning the chicken portions, so that they are evenly browned all over.

2. Add the chopped tomatoes, balsamic vinegar, chicken stock, whole mushrooms and seasoning and bring to the boil. Reduce the heat, cover and simmer for 1½ hours, by which time the chicken should be very tender.

3. Scatter with the basil before serving.

Sesame and pepper chicken parcels

7½ Points per recipe | Takes 25 minutes to prepare, 20 minutes to cook + 20 minutes marinating

Serves 4. Calories per serving 170. Freeze ✓

This is a really colourful and attractive way of serving chicken, adding a bit of fun to the occasion!

2 tablespoons dark soy sauce	1 tablespoon sesame seeds
1 teaspoon sesame oil	8 spring onions
1 garlic clove, crushed	1 red pepper, de-seeded and sliced thinly
1 teaspoon tomato purée	1 green pepper, de-seeded and sliced thinly
350 g (12 oz) skinless, boneless chicken breasts, cut into long thin strips	150 g (5½ oz) carrots, cut into matchsticks

1. In a bowl mix together the soy sauce, sesame oil, crushed garlic and tomato purée. Add the chicken and mix well. Cover and leave to marinate for 20 minutes.

2. Place the sesame seeds in a small saucepan and heat until they turn golden brown. Remove and set them aside.

3. Trim the spring onions, so that you are just left with the green part and then slice thinly. Add the peppers, carrots and the spring onions to the chicken mixture, stirring well.

4. Divide the chicken and vegetables into four portions. Cut four squares of greaseproof paper big enough to parcel up each portion. Spoon the chicken mixture on to the squares and wrap each parcel up tightly.

5. Arrange the parcels in a steamer and cook for 20 minutes.

6. Carefully lift the parcels out of the steamer and unwrap them. Scatter over the toasted sesame seeds and transfer the parcels to four warmed plates to serve.

tip: *If you don't have a steamer, put the parcels in a metal colander or sieve and place over a saucepan of simmering water. Cover the top tightly to prevent the steam from escaping.*

Farmhouse chicken casserole

14 Points per recipe | Takes 30 minutes to prepare, 1 hour to cook

Serves 4. Calories per serving 280. Freeze ✓

This wholesome classic casserole is given a hint of sweetness with an apple.

low fat cooking spray	225 g (8 oz) cooking apple, peeled, cored
450 g (1 lb) skinless chicken breasts, cut	and diced
into bite sized chunks	25 g (1 oz) pearl barley
1 onion, chopped	150 ml (5 fl oz) medium dry cider
225 g (8 oz) carrots, sliced	300 ml (10 fl oz) chicken stock
350 g (12 oz) potatoes, peeled and diced	2 sprigs of fresh thyme or 1 teaspoon
4 celery sticks, sliced	dried thyme
1 tablespoon wholegrain mustard	salt and freshly ground black pepper

1. Heat a large flameproof casserole dish and spray with low fat cooking spray. Add the chicken and stir fry for 2–3 minutes until it is sealed on all sides.

2. Add the onion, carrots, potatoes and celery to the pan and cook for 2 minutes. Stir in the mustard, cooking apple, pearl barley, cider and stock.

3. Season to taste, add the thyme and bring to the boil. Reduce the heat, and cover. Simmer for 1 hour, stirring occasionally, until the pearl barley is tender and the apple has cooked to a pulp, thickening the sauce.

Italian chicken meatballs

13 Points per recipe | Takes 30 minutes to prepare, 40 minutes to cook

Serves 4. Calories per serving 215. Freeze ✓

Meatballs made with chicken mince instead of beef make a lower Point dish, but are just as tasty.

1 teaspoon olive oil	400 g can of chopped tomatoes
1 red onion, chopped very finely	300 ml (10 fl oz) chicken stock
1 garlic clove, crushed	2 tablespoons tomato purée
1 teaspoon dried oregano	3 tablespoons dry white wine
450 g (1 lb) chicken mince	100 g (3½ oz) button mushrooms, sliced
50 g (1¾ oz) fresh white breadcrumbs	salt and freshly ground black pepper
1 egg	

1. Heat the olive oil in a small saucepan and add the onion and garlic with 1 tablespoon of water. Cover and cook over a low heat for 5 minutes, until the onion has softened.

2. Place the oregano, chicken mince, breadcrumbs, egg and seasoning in a mixing bowl with the garlic and onion. Mix thoroughly and then roll the mixture into 20 small balls between the palms of your hands – wet your hands with cold water to prevent the mixture sticking to you.

3. Place the remaining ingredients in a medium saucepan. Stir well and bring to the boil. Add the chicken meatballs and seasoning, reduce the heat, cover and simmer for 40 minutes, stirring from time to time.

tip: *The poached chicken meatballs will have quite a soft texture. For a firmer texture, cook the sauce separately for 15 minutes and arrange the meatballs on a baking sheet lined with baking parchment. Spray with low fat cooking spray and bake at Gas Mark 5/190°C/fan oven 170°C for 20 minutes. Heat them in the sauce for 5 minutes.*

try this: (V) *For a vegetarian version, substitute Quorn mince for the chicken. The Points per serving will be 2½.*

Chicken and broccoli pie

27 Points per recipe | **Takes 40 minutes to prepare, 20 minutes to cook**

Serves 4. Calories per serving 435. Freeze ✓

700 g (1 lb 9 oz) potatoes, peeled and diced

1 tablespoon wholegrain mustard

2 tablespoons 0% fat Greek style
natural yogurt

25 g (1 oz) polyunsaturated margarine

25 g (1 oz) plain white flour

300 ml (10 fl oz) skimmed milk

350 g (12 oz) broccoli, broken into florets

400 g (14 oz) cooked, skinless chicken
breasts, cubed

50 g (1¾ oz) half fat Red Leicester cheese,
grated

salt and freshly ground black pepper

1. Cook the potatoes in lightly salted, boiling water for 15 minutes until tender. Drain and mash thoroughly with the mustard and yogurt.

2. While the potatoes are cooking, melt the margarine in a small saucepan and stir in the flour. Cook, stirring, for 1 minute and then gradually add the milk. Stir until you have a smooth, thickened sauce. Season to taste and simmer for 2 minutes.

3. Preheat the oven to Gas Mark 5/190°C/fan oven 170°C. Cook the broccoli florets for 2 minutes in lightly salted, boiling water and drain thoroughly.

4. Mix the chicken into the sauce along with the broccoli and grated cheese, and stir well. Spoon the mixture into an ovenproof dish and top with the mashed potatoes – using the prongs of a fork to mark a pattern on the top of the mash.

5. Bake for 20 minutes, until piping hot and serve straight away.

tip: *Don't overcook the broccoli or it will go very mushy and lose its attractive colour.*

try this: *This recipe is also ideal for using up any leftover turkey. The Points will be 6½ per serving.*

Chicken drumsticks with gremolata

16 Points per recipe | **Takes 20 minutes to prepare, 25 minutes to cook**

Serves 4. Calories per serving 155. Freeze ✓

Keep a tub of the zesty sauce in the fridge; it will last for three days and is delicious served with grilled meats.

8 x 75 g (2¾ oz) chicken drumsticks,
skinned

1 tablespoon lemon juice

½ teaspoon paprika

For the gremolata:

15 g (½ oz) fresh flat leaf parsley, de-stalked
and chopped very finely

1 garlic clove, crushed

finely grated zest and juice of ½ lemon

2 shallots, chopped very finely

1 teaspoon clear honey

1 teaspoon olive oil

salt and freshly ground black pepper

1. Preheat the oven to Gas Mark 5/190°C/fan oven 170°C. Line a baking tray with non stick baking parchment. Make 2–3 diagonal slits along the top of each chicken drumstick. Lay them on the baking sheet.

2. Mix together the lemon juice and paprika, and brush a little over each drumstick. Roast for 25 minutes, until the chicken is cooked through.

3. Mix together all the ingredients for the gremolata. Serve the cooked chicken with a spoonful of gremolata.

try this: *Use a teaspoon of sesame oil instead of olive oil to add a different flavour to the gremolata. The Points will remain the same.*

Coq au vin

28½ Points per recipe | **Takes 35 minutes to prepare, 1½ hours to cook**

Serves 4. Calories per serving 255. Freeze ✓

This traditional French favourite is literally 'chicken with wine'. This version is lower in Points than the traditional, but just as tasty.

---

75 g (2¾ oz) streaky smoked bacon,
   cut into small pieces

450 g (1 lb) skinless, boneless chicken
   thighs

225 g (8 oz) shallots

225 g (8 oz) baby button mushrooms

300 ml (10 fl oz) chicken stock

150 ml (5 fl oz) red wine

2 bay leaves

2 tablespoons tomato purée

2 tablespoons plain white flour

salt and freshly ground black pepper

2 tablespoons chopped fresh flat leaf
   parsley, to serve

---

1. Heat a large heavy based flameproof casserole dish and add the bacon. Dry fry for 5 minutes, stirring frequently, until the fat has cooked out and the bacon turns crispy.

2. Add the chicken thighs and whole shallots to the pan and cook for 5 minutes, turning half way through, until the chicken has sealed on all sides.

3. Add the mushrooms, stock, wine, bay leaves, tomato purée and seasoning. Stir well and bring to the boil. Reduce the heat, cover, and simmer over a low heat for 1½ hours.

4. Sift the flour into the pan and cook, stirring, until the sauce thickens slightly. Sprinkle with parsley and serve.

try this: *Chicken thighs have a bit more flavour than breast meat which is why they're used in this recipe. Use the same weight of breasts if you prefer; the Points per serving will then be 4.*

goes well with...

a glass of red wine. A 175 ml (6 fl oz) glass is 2 Points.

Asian chicken salad

4 Points per recipe | Takes 25 minutes

Serves 1. Calories per serving 320. Freeze ✗

---

100 g (3½ oz) cooked, skinless chicken
   breast

low fat cooking spray

50 g (1¾ oz) carrots, grated

2 spring onions, sliced into long, thin strips

50 g (1¾ oz) fresh beansprouts

½ small ripe mango, diced

finely grated zest of ½ lime

1 teaspoon crunchy peanut butter

1 teaspoon sweet chilli sauce

50 ml (2 fl oz) pineapple juice

¼ head of Chinese leaves, shredded

---

1. Use two forks to shred the chicken finely. Heat a non stick frying pan and spray it with low fat cooking spray. Add the chicken and stir fry for 3–4 minutes until it is heated through. Add the carrots, spring onions and beansprouts, and cook for a further 2 minutes, until the beansprouts have wilted a little.

2. Add the mango to the pan and stir well. Mix together the lime zest, peanut butter, chilli sauce and pineapple juice, and pour this into the pan. Stir well and cook for 2 minutes, until the sauce bubbles.

3. Arrange the shredded Chinese leaves on a serving plate and top with the hot chicken mixture.

Chicken roulades

8 Points per recipe | Takes 15 minutes to prepare, 25 minutes to cook

Serves 2. Calories per serving 245. Freeze ✓

---

2 x 175 g (6 oz) skinless chicken breasts

75 g (2¾ oz) low fat soft cheese

1 tablespoon finely chopped fresh chives

½ teaspoon Dijon mustard

1 teaspoon sun dried tomato purée

low fat cooking spray

1. Preheat the oven to Gas Mark 4/180°C/fan oven 160°C. Line a baking tray with non stick baking parchment.

2. Place each chicken breast between two pieces of greaseproof paper and, using the flat end of a rolling pin, hammer them out gently to about 1 cm (½ inch) thick. Peel away the greaseproof paper, and lay the breasts flat on a clean work surface.

3. Beat together the soft cheese, chives, mustard and sun dried tomato purée, and spread equal amounts of this mixture over each chicken breast. Loosely roll up the breasts from the narrow end enclosing the filling, and secure with one or two cocktail sticks.

4. Place the chicken rolls on the baking tray and spray with low fat cooking spray. Bake them for 25 minutes.

5. To serve, carefully remove the cocktail sticks. Slice each breast into rings. Arrange on warmed serving plates.

tip: *Hammer out the chicken breasts as evenly as possible without splitting the flesh.*

Indian spiced chicken

21 Points per recipe | Takes 25 minutes to prepare, 25 minutes to cook + 1 hour marinating

Serves 4. Calories per serving 370. Freeze ✓

4 x 125 g (4½ oz) skinless chicken breasts	½ teaspoon salt
100 ml (3½ fl oz) low fat plain yogurt	225 g (8 oz) basmati rice
2 garlic cloves, crushed	50 g (1¾ oz) frozen peas
½ teaspoon turmeric	2 tomatoes, de-seeded and diced
1 teaspoon ground cumin	1 tablespoon chopped fresh mint
2 shallots, chopped very finely	salt
2 tablespoons fresh lemon juice	4 lemon wedges, to serve
2 tablespoons chopped fresh coriander	

1. Score the top of the chicken breasts and arrange them in a shallow non metallic dish. Mix together the yogurt, garlic, turmeric, cumin, shallots, lemon juice, coriander and salt. Spoon this mixture over the chicken, mix well to coat each chicken breast, and then cover and leave to marinate for 1 hour.

2. Preheat the oven to Gas Mark 5/190°C/fan oven 170°C. Line a baking tray with non stick baking parchment and place the marinated chicken breasts on it. Bake in the oven for 25 minutes.

3. Meanwhile, place the rice in a large saucepan with 600 ml (20 fl oz) water and a little salt, and bring to the boil. Reduce the heat, add the peas and simmer for 12 minutes until the rice is tender. Drain well.

4. Stir the diced tomatoes and mint into the rice.

5. Spoon the rice on to warmed plates and top with a chicken breast and a lemon wedge to squeeze over.

tip: *If you prefer your curries hot, add a teaspoon of ground chilli along with the other spices.*

Turkey and vegetable crumble

26 Points per recipe | Takes 20 minutes to prepare, 45 minutes to cook

Serves 4. Calories per serving 415. Freeze ✓

low fat cooking spray	1 tablespoon cornflour
400 g (14 oz) turkey breasts, diced	salt and freshly ground black pepper
150 g (5½ oz) carrots, diced finely	For the crumble:
4 celery sticks, sliced	150 g (5½ oz) plain white flour
350 g (12 oz) leeks, sliced	50 g (1¾ oz) polyunsaturated margarine
300 ml (10 fl oz) chicken stock	50 g (1¾ oz) half fat Cheddar cheese, grated
150 ml (5 fl oz) tomato juice	salt and freshly ground black pepper

1. Heat a large non stick saucepan and spray with low fat cooking spray. Add the turkey and stir fry for 5 minutes, until it is sealed on all sides. Add the carrots, celery and leeks to the pan and cook for a further 5 minutes.

2. Add the stock, tomato juice and seasoning. Bring to the boil, and then cover and simmer for 20 minutes. Mix the cornflour with a little cold water to form a thin paste and stir this into the turkey mixture.

3. Preheat the oven to Gas Mark 5/190°C/fan oven 170°C. Spoon the turkey mixture into an ovenproof dish.

4. To make the crumble, sift the flour into a mixing bowl and rub in the margarine until the mixture resembles fine breadcrumbs. Stir in the cheese and seasoning, and then sprinkle the crumble evenly over the top of the turkey mixture.

5. Bake for 25 minutes, until the crumble topping is golden.

tip: *You could make individual crumbles if you like. You will need to reduce the cooking time by 5 minutes.*

Teriyaki turkey noodles

24 Points per recipe | Takes 25 minutes + 15 minutes standing

Serves 4. Calories per serving 440. Freeze ✓

250 g (9 oz) medium egg noodles	100 g (3½ oz) celery, sliced thinly
600 ml (20 fl oz) boiling chicken stock	125 g (4½ oz) mange tout peas
3 tablespoons Teriyaki sauce	1 bunch of spring onions, shredded
1 tablespoon vegetable oil	2 tablespoons tomato ketchup
450 g (1 lb) turkey breasts, cut into thin strips	2 teaspoons cornflour
175 g (6 oz) carrots, cut into matchsticks	2 tablespoons sherry

1. Place the noodles in a bowl. Pour over the boiling stock. Stir in the Teriyaki sauce and leave for 15 minutes.

2. Meanwhile, heat the oil in a large frying pan or wok and add the turkey strips. Stir fry for about 5 minutes and then add the carrots, celery and mange tout peas. Stir fry for a further 5 minutes.

3. Drain the noodles, reserving the liquid, and add them to the pan or wok, with the spring onions, mixing well. Add the reserved liquid and bring to the boil.

4. Mix together the tomato ketchup, cornflour and sherry, and add this to the pan. Cook, stirring, until the sauce thickens a little, and then serve straight away.

Chicken, leek and sweetcorn pancakes

17 Points per recipe | Takes 40 minutes

Serves 4. Calories per serving 285. Freeze ✗ (see tip)

100 g (3½ oz) plain white flour	350 g (12 oz) skinless chicken breasts, diced
1 egg	225 g (8 oz) leeks, sliced
300 ml (10 fl oz) skimmed milk	1 chicken stock cube
a pinch of salt	4 tablespoons boiling water
low fat cooking spray	125 g (4½ oz) canned sweetcorn, drained
For the filling:	150 ml (5 fl oz) low fat plain fromage frais
low fat cooking spray	salt and freshly ground black pepper

1. To make the pancakes, sift the flour into a mixing bowl. Make a well in the centre and add the egg, milk and salt, and whisk to a smooth batter.

2. Spray a non stick crêpe pan or a 20 cm (8 inch) frying pan with low fat cooking spray. Swirl about a ladleful of the batter into the pan – enough to just cover the bottom of the pan. Cook for 1 minute then flip the pancake over and cook the other side for 1 minute. Repeat until you have eight pancakes. Stack them on a plate, cover with foil and keep them warm while preparing the filling.

3. Heat a non stick frying pan and spray with low fat cooking spray. Add the chicken and leeks and stir fry for 5 minutes until the chicken is sealed on all sides. Crumble in the stock cube and add the boiling water. Stir well and cook for about 5 minutes, uncovered, until all the liquid evaporates.

4. Add the sweetcorn, fromage frais and seasoning, and warm through gently – don't allow it to boil or it may separate.

5. To serve, remove the foil from the pancakes and divide the filling between them. Fill the pancakes just before you are ready to serve, if you assemble them too early they will become soggy. Roll them up and serve hot.

tip: *To freeze the pancakes, stack them between sheets of greaseproof paper, then wrap them in foil. Place in a freezer bag and freeze for up to three months. Defrost at room temperature, then warm through in a frying pan for 1 minute.*

Roast christmas turkey

31 Points per recipe | Takes 40 minutes to prepare, 2 hours to cook

Serves 6. Calories per serving 325. Freeze ✗

2.25 kg (5 lb) turkey

50 g (1¾ oz) streaky bacon rashers

salt and freshly ground black pepper

For the stuffing:

low fat cooking spray

4 shallots, chopped finely

225 g (8 oz) mushrooms, chopped finely

125 g (4½ oz) fresh wholemeal breadcrumbs

2 teaspoons dried tarragon

2 tablespoons reduced sugar marmalade

3 tablespoons fresh orange juice

For the gravy:

300 ml (10 fl oz) chicken stock

2 tablespoons cornflour

2 tablespoons port

---

1. Rinse the turkey well and pat it dry thoroughly with kitchen paper. Place it in a large roasting tin.

2. Preheat the oven to Gas Mark 5/190°C/fan oven 170°C.

3. To make the stuffing, spray a medium saucepan with low fat cooking spray and add the shallots. Cook them gently until softened and then add the mushrooms. Cover and cook gently for 5 minutes until the mushrooms are tender. Remove the pan from the heat and mix in the breadcrumbs, tarragon, marmalade and orange juice. Fill the neck cavity of the turkey with the stuffing and then pull the neck flap of skin over the stuffing and tuck it under the bird, securing it with a cocktail stick. Season it well with salt and freshly ground black pepper, and lay the bacon rashers over the breast in a criss-cross pattern.

4. Roast the turkey for 2 hours. When cooked, carefully lift it out of the roasting tin on to a large serving platter. Allow it to rest for 10 minutes before carving.

5. For the gravy, pour the turkey juices into a pan – skim off the fat first. Stir in the stock and bring it to the boil. Mix the cornflour with the port and stir this in. Cook, stirring, until the gravy thickens.

6. Thinly carve the turkey and serve 150 g (5½ oz) of meat per person with 50 g (1¾ oz) of the stuffing, your chosen zero Point vegetables and the gravy.

Tarragon chicken with mushrooms

11 Points per recipe | Takes 30 minutes

Serves 2. Calories per serving 300. Freeze ✗

---

2 teaspoons sunflower oil

2 x 150 g (5½ oz) skinless chicken breasts,
   cut into thin strips

150 g (5½ oz) mushrooms, sliced

2 teaspoons chopped fresh tarragon or
   1 teaspoon dried tarragon

3 tablespoons sherry

150 ml (5 fl oz) chicken stock

1 tablespoon cornflour

2 tablespoons half fat crème fraîche

salt and freshly ground black pepper

---

1. Heat the oil in a non stick frying pan and add the chicken strips. Stir fry for 5 minutes until the chicken is sealed on all sides. Add the mushrooms and tarragon and cook for a further 2 minutes.

2. Season to taste, and add the sherry and stock. Bring to the boil, and then cover and simmer for 10 minutes.

3. Mix the cornflour with a little cold water to make a thin paste and stir it into the sauce. Cook, stirring, until the sauce thickens a little. Remove from the heat, stir in the crème fraîche and serve immediately.

tip: *This is delicious served with freshly cooked tagliatelle. A 150 g (5½ oz) portion of cooked pasta has 2 Points.*

Lime and ginger chicken

5 Points per recipe | Takes 25 minutes

Serves 2. Calories per serving 260. Freeze ✓

The vibrant, fresh flavours of ginger and lime bring this tasty stir fry to life.

1 teaspoon sunflower oil

225 g (8 oz) skinless chicken breasts,
    cut into thin strips

1 red chilli, de-seeded and chopped finely

1 garlic clove, crushed

2.5 cm (1 inch) piece of root ginger, peeled
    and grated

finely grated zest of 1 lime

2 tablespoons light soy sauce

1 teaspoon clear honey

175 g (6 oz) white cabbage, shredded

100 g (3½ oz) mange tout peas, halved

6 spring onions, sliced into thin strips

75 g (2¾ oz) canned water chestnuts,
    drained and sliced

150 g (5½ oz) carrots

150 ml (5 fl oz) chicken stock

1 teaspoon cornflour

2 tablespoons fresh lime juice

1. Heat the sunflower oil in a non stick wok or large frying pan and add the chicken. Stir fry for 4–5 minutes to seal it on all sides. Add the chilli, garlic, ginger, lime zest, soy sauce and honey, and stir fry until it is all bubbling.

2. Add the cabbage, mange tout peas, spring onions, and water chestnuts, and stir fry for 2 minutes. Using a swivel head peeler, peel the carrots into thin ribbons and add these to the pan.

3. Pour in the stock and bring to the boil. Cook over a high heat for 3 minutes. Mix the cornflour with the lime juice to make a paste and stir this into the pan. Cook, stirring, until the juices thicken a little, and then serve at once.

Chicken with black bean and pineapple salsa

11 Points per recipe | Takes 25 minutes

Serves 4. Calories per serving 205. Freeze ✗

Salsas are an excellent way to liven up grilled meat, chicken or fish and this one is particularly good!

450 g (1 lb) skinless, boneless chicken
    breasts

1 garlic clove, halved

low fat cooking spray

salt and freshly ground black pepper

For the salsa:

1 red onion, chopped very finely

2 tablespoons red wine vinegar

1 teaspoon caster sugar

2 teaspoons extra virgin olive oil

3 tablespoons chopped fresh flat leaf
    parsley

100 g (3½ oz) canned pineapple in natural
    juice, drained and chopped finely

125 g (4½ oz) canned black beans, drained
    and rinsed

1. Season the chicken breasts and rub the cut sides of the halved garlic over each breast. Spray them with low fat cooking spray. Place the chicken under a medium grill and cook for 5–6 minutes on each side, until it is cooked through.

2. Meanwhile, make the salsa. Place the red onion in a mixing bowl with the vinegar, sugar, olive oil and parsley, and stir together well. Add the chopped pineapple and black beans, and mix together thoroughly. Cover the bowl and leave it to stand until you are ready to serve it with the grilled chicken.

try this: *There are a huge variety of canned beans available in our shops these days; the black beans in this recipe contrast wonderfully against the red onion and green parsley. Try experimenting with other beans such as red kidney or borlotti. Alter the Points accordingly.*

Sticky chicken bites

5½ Points per recipe | **Takes 40 minutes + 30 minutes marinating**

Serves 2. Calories per serving 215. Freeze ✓

2 x 150 g (5½ oz) skinless chicken breasts, cut into bite size pieces	½ teaspoon Chinese five spice powder
2 tablespoons tomato ketchup	1 teaspoon clear honey
2 tablespoons dark soy sauce	2 celery sticks, sliced thinly
	1 carrot, sliced into thin rings

1. Place the chicken in a shallow dish. Mix together the tomato ketchup, soy sauce, five spice powder and honey, and drizzle it over the chicken. Mix well, cover and leave it to marinate for 30 minutes.
2. Preheat the oven to Gas Mark 5/190°C/fan oven 170°C. Line a baking tray with non stick baking parchment.
3. Mix the celery and carrot with the chicken and then arrange the coated pieces on the baking tray. Bake for 25 minutes, until the chicken is cooked through and the marinade has formed a sticky glaze.

Pesto chicken

10 Points per recipe | **Takes 15 minutes to prepare, 30 minutes to cook**

Serves 2. Calories per serving 295. Freeze ✓

2 x 150 g (5½ oz) skinless chicken breasts	1 beefsteak tomato, sliced
4 large fresh basil leaves	1 tablespoon grated Parmesan cheese
1 tablespoon pesto sauce	salt and freshly ground black pepper
75 g (2¾ oz) low fat soft cheese	

1. Preheat the oven to Gas Mark 5/190°C/fan oven 170°C.
2. Make a slit along the length of each chicken breast and push two basil leaves into each slit.
3. Beat together the pesto and soft cheese and spread this mixture on top of each chicken breast. Season and then lay the chicken in a shallow ovenproof dish. Top with a layer of tomato slices.
4. Sprinkle the Parmesan cheese over the top and bake in the oven for 30 minutes. Serve hot.

Club sandwich

9½ Points per recipe | **Takes 15 minutes**

Serves 2. Calories per serving 405. Freeze ✓

2 rashers lean back bacon	4 Little Gem lettuce leaves, shredded
1 tablespoon low fat mayonnaise	1 tomato, sliced
½ teaspoon Dijon mustard	15 g (½ oz) dolcelatte cheese, crumbled
3 medium slices white bread	salt and freshly ground black pepper
25 g (1 oz) wafer thin turkey	

1. Grill the bacon and drain it on kitchen paper. Combine the mayonnaise and mustard and spread this on the bread.
2. Arrange half the turkey on one slice of the bread, top with 2 lettuce leaves, a bacon rasher and half the tomato slices. Place the second slice of bread on top and then top with the rest of the turkey, bacon, lettuce and tomatoes, cheese and seasoning. Cover with the last slice of bread, cut into quarters and secure each with a cocktail stick.

3 POINTS

Chicken and mango stir fry

6 Points per recipe | Takes 30 minutes

Serves 2. Calories per serving 335. Freeze ✓

Stir frying a colourful mix of vegetables always looks attractive and what's more tastes great.

low fat cooking spray

225 g (8 oz) skinless chicken breasts,
   cut into strips

1 garlic clove, crushed

1 fresh red chilli, de-seeded and chopped
   finely

2.5 cm (1 inch) piece of root ginger, peeled
   and grated

175 g (6 oz) broccoli, broken into florets

125 g (4½ oz) mange tout peas

125 g (4½ oz) baby sweetcorn, halved

100 g (3½ oz) canned bamboo shoots,
   drained

225 g (8 oz) peeled and cubed mango

4 tablespoons ginger wine

2 tablespoons tomato purée

2 tablespoons soy sauce

1 teaspoon cornflour

1. Heat a large non stick frying pan or wok and spray it with low fat cooking spray. Add the chicken strips and stir fry for 5 minutes until the chicken has browned evenly.

2. Add the garlic, chilli, ginger, broccoli, mange tout peas and baby sweetcorn, and stir fry for a further 5 minutes.

3. Add the bamboo shoots and mango, and heat through for 2 minutes.

4. Mix together the ginger wine, tomato purée, soy sauce and cornflour, and add this to the pan. Cook, stirring, until the sauce thickens. Spoon on to warmed plates and serve.

try this: **V** *You could use cubes of finely diced tofu instead of chicken. This will be 2½ Points per serving.*

goes well with...

freshly cooked noodles, adding 2 Points for a 150 g (5½ oz) serving.

beef...
lamb and pork

7½ POINTS

Beef en croûte

15 Points per recipe | **Takes 25 minutes to prepare, 20 minutes to cook**

Serves 2. Calories per serving 425. Freeze ✓

This dish looks very impressive so it is well worth the effort for a special occasion.

1 teaspoon sunflower oil	15 g (½ oz) fresh white breadcrumbs
2 x 125 g (4½ oz) beef fillet steaks	4 sheets filo pastry
2 large open cup mushrooms	15 g (½ oz) low fat spread, melted
25 g (1 oz) dolcelatte cheese, crumbled	salt and freshly ground black pepper

1. Heat the sunflower oil in a non stick frying pan and fry the steaks for 1 minute on each side to seal them. Remove the steaks from the pan.

2. Remove the stalks from the mushrooms and set them aside. Add the mushrooms to the pan, cup side down. Cook them for 2 minutes until they begin to soften and then drain them on kitchen paper.

3. Chop the mushroom stalks very finely and mix them with the cheese, breadcrumbs and seasoning. Pack this mixture into the cup of the mushrooms, pressing down well. Place a mushroom, filled side down, on top of each steak.

4. Preheat the oven to Gas Mark 6/200°C/fan oven 180°C. Line a baking tray with non stick baking parchment.

5. Brush each sheet of filo pastry with the melted low fat spread and stack two sheets together, so you have two piles of pastry. Wrap each mushroom topped steak in a double layer of pastry and brush the surface with any remaining melted spread.

6. Bake in the oven for 20 minutes until the pastry is crisp and golden.

Lamb hotpot

15½ Points per recipe | Takes 30 minutes to prepare, 2 hours to cook

Serves 4. Calories per serving 390. Freeze ✓

450 g (1 lb) lamb chops

2 onions, sliced

350 g (12 oz) carrots, sliced

6 celery sticks, sliced

600 ml (20 fl oz) lamb stock

2 tablespoons Worcestershire sauce

2 bay leaves

450 g (1 lb) potatoes, peeled and sliced
thinly

1 bulb of fennel, shredded thinly

low fat cooking spray

salt and freshly ground black pepper

1. Heat a heavy based, flameproof casserole dish and add the lamb chops. Dry fry for 2 minutes on each side to seal and lightly brown them.

2. Add the onions, carrots and celery to the pan. Pour over the stock and stir in the Worcestershire sauce, bay leaves and seasoning. Bring to the boil.

3. Preheat the oven to Gas Mark 3/160°C/fan oven 140°C. Remove the casserole dish from the heat and arrange the sliced potatoes and shredded fennel over the top of the lamb.

4. Spray the top evenly with low fat cooking spray, and cover the dish with a sheet of foil or a tight fitting lid. Cook for 1 hour, and then remove the cover and cook for a further 1 hour, until the meat is very tender and the potatoes and fennel have lightly browned.

Shepherd's pie

23 Points per recipe | Takes 25 minutes to prepare, 1 hour 10 minutes to cook

Serves 4. Calories per serving 365. Freeze ✓

350 g (12 oz) lean lamb mince

1 onion, chopped finely

175 g (6 oz) mushrooms, chopped finely

175 g (6 oz) cooking apple, peeled, cored
and grated

2 tablespoons tomato purée

225 g can of chopped tomatoes

300 ml (10 fl oz) lamb stock

450 g (1 lb) potatoes, peeled and diced

350 g (12 oz) carrots, chopped

15 g (½ oz) polyunsaturated margarine

2 spring onions, sliced

salt and freshly ground black pepper

1. Heat a heavy based, non stick frying pan and add the lamb. Dry fry, stirring, until the mince is crumbly and evenly browned. Add the onion, mushrooms and apple, and cook for 5 minutes.

2. Stir in the tomato purée, chopped tomatoes, stock and seasoning, and bring to the boil. Reduce the heat, cover, and simmer for 30 minutes.

3. Meanwhile, bring a large saucepan of lightly salted water to the boil, and add the potatoes and carrots. Cook them for 20 minutes until they are tender.

4. Heat the margarine in a small saucepan and add the spring onions. Cook for 2–3 minutes until softened.

5. Drain the potatoes and carrots and mash them thoroughly with the spring onions.

6. Preheat the oven to Gas Mark 6/200°C/fan oven 180°C. Spoon the lamb mixture into an ovenproof dish and top with the potato mixture. Bake for 25 minutes, until the shepherd's pie is bubbling.

try this: **V** *You can make this dish using vegetarian mince which doesn't need to be cooked for so long. Simmer the sauce for only 10 minutes and bake the dish in the oven for 20 minutes. Points will be reduced to 4½ per serving.*

Lamb steaks with port and mint sauce

9 Points per recipe | **Takes 20 minutes to prepare, 25 minutes to cook**

Serves 2. Calories per serving 400. Freeze ✓

low fat cooking spray

2 x 150 g (5½ oz) boneless lamb leg steaks

1 red onion, sliced

300 ml (10 fl oz) lamb stock

2 tablespoons port

2 teaspoons redcurrant jelly

2 teaspoons cornflour

1 tablespoon chopped fresh mint

salt and freshly ground black pepper

1. Heat a large non stick frying pan and spray with low fat cooking spray. Add the lamb steaks to the pan and cook for 2 minutes on each side to seal and brown them.

2. Add the onion to the pan and cook for a further 5 minutes, until it begins to brown lightly. Stir in the stock, port and redcurrant jelly and bring to the boil. Reduce the heat, cover and simmer for 20 minutes.

3. Mix the cornflour with a little cold water to make a thin paste and add this to the pan. Cook, stirring, until the sauce thickens a little. Season and stir in the mint. Serve at once.

tip: *If you don't have a lid to your frying pan you can either transfer the ingredients to a saucepan after frying the steaks and onion, or use a baking tray to cover the top of the pan. Take care when lifting the baking tray off, use a tea towel or oven glove as it will get very hot.*

Moroccan spiced lamb

15 Points per recipe | **Takes 20 minutes to prepare, 1¼ hours to cook**

Serves 4. Calories per serving 340. Freeze ✓

450 g (1 lb) lamb leg steaks, trimmed of fat
   and cubed

1 tablespoon plain white flour

½ teaspoon ground cinnamon

1 teaspoon ground cumin

1 teaspoon paprika

1 teaspoon ground coriander

1 tablespoon olive oil

1 onion, sliced

2 garlic cloves, crushed

1 red pepper, de-seeded and diced

225 g (8 oz) courgettes, sliced

50 g (1¾ oz) ready to eat dried apricots,
   chopped

400 g can of chopped tomatoes

300 ml (10 fl oz) lamb stock

salt and freshly ground black pepper

2 tablespoons chopped fresh mint, to serve

1. Place the lamb in a polythene bag with the flour, cinnamon, cumin, paprika and coriander. Shake the bag well to coat the lamb with a dusting of spices.

2. Heat the oil in a large non stick frying pan, add the lamb and cook for 5 minutes, stirring, until it is sealed on all sides.

3. Add the onion, garlic, pepper, courgettes, apricots, chopped tomatoes and stock and bring to the boil. Season to taste. Reduce the heat, cover and simmer for 1 hour.

4. Remove the cover from the pan. Turn up the heat and allow the sauce to bubble quite hard for 10 minutes to reduce a little of the liquid.

5. Sprinkle over the mint and serve.

try this: *To spice up this dish, add two de-seeded and finely chopped fresh green chillies in step 3.*

Moussaka

28½ Points per recipe | **Takes 45 minutes to prepare, 35 minutes to cook**

Serves 4. Calories per serving 450. Freeze ✓

This traditional Greek favourite can be very high in Points. We've created a low Point version, but haven't lost the superb flavour! Serve with a Greek style salad of Cos lettuce, cucumber and tomatoes.

350 g (12 oz) lean lamb mince	1 aubergine, sliced thinly
1 red onion, chopped finely	25 g (1 oz) polyunsaturated margarine
2 garlic cloves, crushed	25 g (1 oz) plain white flour
1 teaspoon dried oregano	300 ml (10 fl oz) skimmed milk
400 g can of chopped tomatoes	150 ml (5 fl oz) 0% fat Greek style natural
2 tablespoons tomato purée	yogurt
150 ml (5 fl oz) lamb stock	a pinch of ground nutmeg
50 g (1¾ oz) dried, split red lentils	2 beefsteak tomatoes, sliced
350 g (12 oz) potatoes, sliced thinly	salt and freshly ground black pepper

1. Dry fry the lamb mince in a large, heavy based frying pan until it is evenly browned. Add the onion, garlic and oregano, stir well and cook for 2 minutes.

2. Add the chopped tomatoes, tomato purée, stock, lentils and seasoning, and bring to the boil. Reduce the heat, cover and simmer for 25 minutes, until the lentils have become tender and most of the liquid has been absorbed.

3. Meanwhile, cook the potato slices in lightly salted, boiling water for 8–10 minutes until tender. Drain well. Cook the aubergine slices in lightly salted, boiling water for 5 minutes, and then drain well.

4. Melt the margarine in a small non stick saucepan, stir in the flour and cook for 1 minute. Gradually add the milk and cook, stirring, until you have a smooth sauce. Remove from the heat, whisk in the yogurt, nutmeg, and seasoning to taste.

5. Preheat the oven to Gas Mark 4/180°C/fan oven 160°C. Spoon the lamb mixture into an ovenproof dish and arrange the potato slices on top, followed by the aubergine slices. Pour over the sauce and arrange the slices of tomato on top.

6. Bake in the oven for 35 minutes, until the topping is golden and bubbling.

Lamb and mushroom stir fry with oyster sauce

14 Points per recipe | **Takes 30 minutes**

Serves 2. Calories per serving 260. Freeze ✓

Cooking the vegetables on a high heat for a short time ensures they keep their colour and a good crisp texture.

175 g (6 oz) lean lamb neck fillet, trimmed of any fat	100 g (3½ oz) sugar snap peas, sliced in half diagonally
low fat cooking spray	2 tablespoons oyster sauce
1 red onion, sliced into thin wedges	1 tablespoon dark soy sauce
175 g (6 oz) mushrooms, sliced	100 g (3½ oz) fresh beansprouts

1. Cut the lamb into very thin, disc shaped slices. Spray a large non stick frying pan with low fat cooking spray and stir fry the lamb for 5 minutes.

2. Add the onion, mushrooms and sugar snap peas and stir fry them over a high heat for 5 minutes. Add the oyster sauce, soy sauce and beansprouts. Cook until the beansprouts soften and the sauce is bubbling, then serve.

tip: *You should never wash mushrooms as this will make them soggy, just wipe them with kitchen paper.*

Rosemary redcurrant lamb

13 Points per recipe | Takes 15 minutes to prepare, 25-35 minutes to cook

Serves 2. Calories per serving 330. Freeze ✓

When you need something special for a cosy, intimate dinner for two, try this recipe as it looks stunning and tastes divine.

2 x 125 g (4½ oz) lamb loins

25 g (1 oz) fresh white breadcrumbs

2 tablespoons redcurrant jelly

1 teaspoon finely chopped fresh rosemary

2 thin cut streaky bacon rashers

1 teaspoon olive oil

salt and freshly ground black pepper

1. Preheat the oven to Gas Mark 5/190°C/fan oven 170°C.

2. Make a 2.5 cm (1 inch) slit along the top of each lamb loin – the slit should be fairly deep.

3. Mix together the breadcrumbs, redcurrant jelly and rosemary, and then spread this mixture into the split in each lamb loin.

4. Stretch and flatten each bacon rasher with the back of a knife. Now wrap a stretched rasher around each loin, this helps to keep the filling in.

5. Brush each lamb parcel with a little olive oil and then season. Roast for 25 minutes if you like your lamb slightly pink, or 35 minutes if you prefer your lamb well cooked.

tip: *When presenting this dish, slice the cooked lamb into thin rings cut slightly on a slant, and arrange the slices on a bed of freshly cooked zero Point vegetables.*

Valentine's Day

Impress the one you love for just a few Points for the whole meal.

Spicy Thai style sweetcorn soup *page 8*, 1 serving........1½ Points

Rosemary redcurrant lamb *above*, 1 serving..............6½ Points
(pictured right)

Baked nectarines with ricotta and amaretti
   biscuits *page 166*, 1 serving...................3 Points

Total Points for meal...................**11 Points**

Minced lamb kebabs

11½ Points per recipe | Takes 25 minutes

Serves 2. Calories per serving 280. Freeze ✓

200 g (7 oz) lamb mince

1 garlic clove, chopped

1 tablespoon tomato purée

½ teaspoon cumin seeds

½ red pepper, de-seeded and diced very finely

1 small egg, beaten

25 g (1 oz) fresh white breadcrumbs

1 tablespoon chopped fresh coriander

salt and freshly ground black pepper

For the dip:

100 ml (3½ fl oz) low fat plain yogurt

1 tablespoon chopped fresh coriander

finely grated zest of ½ lemon

1. Place the lamb mince in a mixing bowl with the garlic, tomato purée, cumin seeds, red pepper, egg, breadcrumbs, fresh coriander and seasoning. Using clean hands, mix everything together thoroughly and then shape the mixture into eight small meatballs.

2. Take two skewers and thread four meatballs on to each. Grill the kebabs under a medium heat for 10 minutes. Turn them regularly, until they are evenly browned and cooked through.

3. For the dip, whisk together the yogurt, coriander and lemon zest. Spoon the dip into a small bowl, then cover and chill until required.

4. Drizzle the dip over the cooked meatballs and serve.

try this: *This mixture also makes a superb burger, just shape the mince mixture into two round flat burgers and grill them for 5 minutes on each side. Serve the dip as a tasty relish.*

Hearty lamb stew

18 Points per recipe | Takes 30 minutes to prepare, 2 hours to cook

Serves 4. Calories per serving 340. Freeze ✓

This is an ideal dish to make if you have a slow cooker. Prepare it in the morning before you go out and you'll come home to a warming supper that's all ready to serve.

2 tablespoons plain white flour

450 g (1 lb) lean leg of lamb steaks, trimmed of fat and cut into cubes

2 teaspoons sunflower oil

1 onion, sliced

350 g (12 oz) carrots, sliced thickly

6 celery sticks, sliced

350 g (12 oz) baby new potatoes, scrubbed

2 fresh thyme sprigs or 1 teaspoon dried thyme

600 ml (20 fl oz) lamb stock

2 tablespoons tomato purée

salt and freshly ground black pepper

1. Place the flour in a polythene bag and add the lamb cubes. Shake the bag to coat the meat in a fine dusting of flour.

2. Heat the oil in a large, flameproof casserole dish and add the floured lamb. Stir fry for 2–3 minutes to seal it and then add the onion, carrots, celery, potatoes, thyme and seasoning.

3. Add the stock, stir in the tomato purée and bring to the boil. Reduce the heat, cover and simmer for 2 hours, stirring from time to time.

4. Ladle the casserole into four warmed bowls to serve.

tip: *If are using a slow cooker for this dish, prepare it as above but as soon as you have brought it to the boil in step 3, transfer it to the slow cooker for 8 hours.*

Greek roast lamb

21 Points per recipe | Takes 30 minutes to prepare, 2½ hours to cook

Serves 4. Calories per serving 410. Freeze ✓

Long, slow cooking ensures that the meat literally falls off the bone in succulent chunks – delicious!

1 kg (2 lb 4 oz) half leg of lamb	1 onion, cut into wedges
1 head of garlic, divided into cloves but unpeeled	1 aubergine, diced
	1 red pepper, de-seeded and diced
juice of 1 orange	1 green pepper, de-seeded and diced
100 ml (3½ fl oz) red wine	400 g can of chopped tomatoes
2 sprigs of fresh rosemary	salt and freshly ground black pepper

1. Preheat the oven to Gas Mark 5/190°C/fan oven 170°C. Rinse the lamb and pat it dry with kitchen paper. Put it in a roasting tin and scatter the garlic cloves around it. Pour over the orange juice and red wine, arrange the rosemary sprigs on top, and then season the lamb with salt and freshly ground black pepper.

2. Roast the lamb, uncovered, for 1 hour. Remove it from the oven and reduce the heat to Gas Mark 3/160°C/fan oven 140°C. Carefully remove the garlic cloves and set them aside. Skim off any fat from the cooking juices. Squeeze out the pulp from about four of the roasted garlic cloves and spread this over the lamb.

3. In a large bowl, mix together the onion wedges, aubergine, peppers and chopped tomatoes. Spoon this mixture around the lamb and then cover the roasting tin with foil – making sure there are no gaps. Return the lamb to the oven for 1½ hours.

4. Serve the lamb on warmed plates, allowing 125 g (4½ oz) of meat per person.

tip: *Squeeze the pulp from the leftover garlic and you'll get a delicious paste. Keep the paste in a small jar in the fridge for a few days. Add to salad dressings, stews and soups.*

One pot beef with baby vegetables

23 Points per recipe | Takes 25 minutes to prepare, 1 hour 40 minutes to cook

Serves 4. Calories per serving 245. Freeze ✓

This is a great dish to prepare the night before and everything goes in the one pot so you save on washing up too!

1 kg (2 lb 4 oz) silverside joint	225 g (8 oz) shallots, peeled
1 teaspoon sunflower oil	225 g (8 oz) baby carrots, scrubbed
300 ml (10 fl oz) real ale	225 g (8 oz) baby new potatoes, scrubbed
300 ml (10 fl oz) beef stock	225 g (8 oz) baby leeks, halved
2 tablespoons tomato purée	salt and freshly ground black pepper
2 bay leaves	

1. Rinse the silverside joint and pat it dry with kitchen paper. Heat the sunflower oil in a large flameproof casserole dish and add the joint. Cook it on all sides for 2–3 minutes, to seal it.

2. Pour the ale and stock into the dish, and add the tomato purée, bay leaves and seasoning. Bring to the boil and then add the shallots, carrots and new potatoes. Reduce the heat, cover and simmer for 1 hour.

3. Remove the cover, stir, and then add the leeks. Cover and cook for a further 40 minutes. Serve 100 g (3½ oz) thinly sliced beef per person with the vegetables and gravy spooned over.

tip: *Horseradish sauce goes well with this dish. 1 tablespoon has ½ a Point.*

Chilli con carne

19½ Points per recipe | Takes 25 minutes to prepare, 1 hour to cook

Serves 4. Calories per serving 305. Freeze ✓

350 g (12 oz) extra lean beef mince

1 tablespoon mild chilli powder

1 teaspoon ground coriander

1 onion, chopped

2 garlic cloves, crushed

175 g (6 oz) carrots, diced finely

100 g (3½ oz) button mushrooms, quartered

100 ml (3½ fl oz) red wine

400 g can of chopped tomatoes

2 tablespoons tomato purée

300 ml (10 fl oz) beef stock

410 g can of red kidney beans, drained
    and rinsed

salt and freshly ground black pepper

2 tablespoons chopped fresh parsley,
    to garnish

1. Heat a large non stick saucepan and add the mince. Dry fry for 2–3 minutes until the mince is browned. Add the chilli powder, ground coriander, onion, garlic, carrots and mushrooms, and stir well. Cook, stirring, for 5 minutes.

2. Pour in the wine, chopped tomatoes, tomato purée and stock, season, stir well and bring to the boil. Reduce the heat and simmer, stirring from time to time, for 1 hour.

3. About 5 minutes before the end of the cooking time, stir in the kidney beans. Allow them to heat through.

4. Ladle the chilli con carne into warmed bowls. Sprinkle with chopped fresh parsley and serve.

tip: *Make this as hot as you want, but take care! Add a little chilli powder first and then taste before adding more, it's worth remembering that the heat of the chilli develops as it cooks.*

try this: **V** *To make a vegetarian version of this chilli con carne, use vegetarian mince and a vegetable stock cube. You'll only need to cook the chilli for 30 minutes. The Points per serving will be 4.*

goes well with...

a medium jacket potato for an extra 2½ Points per serving.

Roast beef with all the trimmings

37½ Points per recipe | **Takes 1 hour**

Serves 4. Calories per serving 530. Freeze ✗

Sunday wouldn't be complete without a roast, and this recipe means you can enjoy it without using too many Points.

600 g (1 lb 5 oz) piece of beef silverside

salt and freshly ground black pepper

For the roast vegetables:

450 g (1 lb) potatoes, peeled and diced

350 g (12 oz) carrots, cut into large chunks

225 g (8 oz) small parsnips, cut into
   quarters

1 tablespoon sunflower oil

1 teaspoon chilli flakes

salt and freshly ground black pepper

For the Yorkshire puddings:

100 g (3½ oz) plain white flour

a pinch of salt

1 egg

300 ml (10 fl oz) skimmed milk

low fat cooking spray

For the gravy:

425 ml (15 fl oz) beef stock

1 teaspoon horseradish sauce

2 tablespoons cornflour

1. Preheat the oven to Gas Mark 5/190°C/fan oven 170°C. Rinse the beef and place it in a non stick roasting tin. Season well and roast for 1 hour.

2. Meanwhile, in a large mixing bowl, mix together the vegetables with the oil, a little seasoning and the chilli flakes. After 20 minutes of roasting time remove the beef from the oven and arrange the vegetables around it. Return the beef and vegetables to the oven.

3. For the Yorkshire puddings, sift the flour into a mixing bowl and make a well in the centre. Add the salt, egg and milk and whisk to form a smooth batter. Spray a 12 hole, non stick Yorkshire pudding tin with low fat cooking spray and heat it in the top shelf of the oven for 5 minutes. Carefully remove it from the oven and pour in the batter. Cook on the top shelf of the oven for 20 minutes. Time the Yorkshire puddings so they are ready at the same time as the beef.

4. When the meat and vegetables are cooked, carefully transfer them to a warmed serving platter. Pour any cooking juices into a small saucepan and skim off any fat. Add the beef stock and horseradish sauce, and heat until bubbling. Mix the cornflour with a little cold water to make a thin paste and stir it into the pan. Cook, stirring, until the gravy thickens.

5. Serve 100 g (3½ oz) of roast beef per person with the Yorkshire puddings, vegetables and gravy.

Chargrilled beefburgers

14 Points per recipe | **Takes 25 minutes**

Serves 2. Calories per serving 370. Freeze ✓

225 g (8 oz) extra lean beef mince

1 teaspoon wholegrain mustard

25 g (1 oz) pickled gherkins, chopped finely

1 small egg, beaten

25 g (1 oz) fresh white breadcrumbs

low fat cooking spray

salt and freshly ground black pepper

To serve:

2 burger buns, split

salad leaves, shredded

1. Place the mince in a mixing bowl and break it up with your hands. Add the mustard, gherkins, egg, breadcrumbs and seasoning, and mix thoroughly. Using your hands, shape the mixture into two round, flat burgers.

2. Preheat a griddle pan and spray it with low fat cooking spray. When the pan is hot add the burgers and cook them for 5 minutes on each side, or cook them under a hot grill for the same amount of time.

3. Place each beefburger in a bun with some shredded salad leaves and serve at once.

Teriyaki beef with ginger noodles

14 Points per recipe | **Takes 35 minutes**

Serves 2. Calories per serving 475. Freeze ✓

When you feel like spoiling yourself with fillet steak, this succulent dish fits the bill perfectly!

125 g (4½ oz) medium egg noodles

225 g (8 oz) fillet steak

3 tablespoons Teriyaki sauce

1 tablespoon tomato purée

1 garlic clove, crushed

1 tablespoon sherry

2 teaspoons sunflower oil

2.5 cm (1 inch) piece of root ginger, peeled and chopped finely

150 g (5½ oz) shiitake mushrooms, halved

100 g (3½ oz) canned bamboo shoots, drained

3 spring onions, sliced into long, thin strips

1. Place the noodles in a bowl and pour over boiling water. Leave them to stand for 15 minutes.

2. Meanwhile, slice the steak as thinly as you can. Place the beef slices in a shallow dish with the Teriyaki sauce, tomato purée, garlic and sherry. Mix well so that the steak slices are evenly coated in the mixture. Leave the meat for 10 minutes to marinate.

3. Heat the sunflower oil in a non stick frying pan or wok. Drain the beef, reserving any marinade, and add it to the pan with the ginger. Stir fry for 2 minutes and then add the mushrooms, bamboo shoots, most of the spring onions and the reserved marinade.

4. Drain the noodles and add them to the pan. Mix them in well and heat through for 2–3 minutes. Serve at once, sprinkled with remaining spring onions.

Beef stew with beer

13½ Points per recipe | **Takes 30 minutes to prepare, 2 hours to cook**

Serves 4. Calories per serving 290. Freeze ✓

low fat cooking spray

450 g (1 lb) lean braising steak, cubed

225 g (8 oz) baby onions

350 g (12 oz) swede, diced

225 g (8 oz) carrots, cut into chunks

2 celery sticks, sliced

150 g (5½ oz) baby button mushrooms

300 ml (10 fl oz) dark beer or stout

300 ml (10 fl oz) beef stock

2 tablespoons tomato purée

1 teaspoon caster sugar

2 bay leaves

salt and freshly ground black pepper

1. Heat a large flameproof casserole dish and spray it with low fat cooking spray. Add the braising steak and cook it over a high heat for 5 minutes to seal it on all sides.

2. Add the onions, swede, carrots, celery and mushrooms, and cook for a further 5 minutes.

3. Pour over the beer or stout and the stock. Stir in the tomato purée, sugar, bay leaves and seasoning, and bring to the boil. Reduce the heat, cover and simmer over a very gentle heat, stirring from time to time, for 2 hours. Serve on four warmed plates.

tip: *Use a dark beer for this dish to ensure that the gravy ends up a rich deep colour.*

Lasagne

33 Points per recipe | **Takes 45 minutes to prepare, 35 minutes to cook**

Serves 4. Calories per serving 535. Freeze ✓

It really is worth making your own low Point lasagne. Not only will it taste better than a shop bought version, but you'll find you get a bigger portion of lasagne for your Points.

350 g (12 oz) extra lean beef mince	150 ml (5 fl oz) beef stock
1 onion, chopped finely	225 g (8 oz) no pre cook lasagne sheets
2 garlic cloves, crushed	salt and freshly ground black pepper
225 g (8 oz) carrots, grated	For the sauce:
100 g (3½ oz) button mushrooms, chopped	25 g (1 oz) polyunsaturated margarine
400 g can of chopped tomatoes	25 g (1 oz) plain white flour
2 tablespoons tomato purée	300 ml (10 fl oz) skimmed milk
1 teaspoon mixed dried herbs	25 g (1 oz) Parmesan cheese, grated

1. Heat a large non stick saucepan and add the mince. Dry fry, stirring, until the mince has evenly browned. Add the onion, garlic, carrots and mushrooms and cook, stirring, for 5 minutes. Add the chopped tomatoes, tomato purée, herbs, stock and seasoning, and bring to the boil. Cover and simmer for 20 minutes.

2. Preheat the oven to Gas Mark 4/180°C/fan oven 160°C. To make the sauce, heat the margarine in a medium size saucepan. Stir in the flour. Gradually add the milk and cook, stirring, until it is a smooth and thick. Stir in half the Parmesan cheese.

3. To assemble the lasagne, spoon half the mince mixture into a rectangular ovenproof dish and top with half the lasagne sheets. Spoon half the cheese sauce over the top, and then the remaining mince followed by the remaining lasagne sheets. Finish with a final layer of cheese sauce. Sprinkle the remaining half of the Parmesan cheese over the top and bake in the oven for 35 minutes.

4. Cut the lasagne into square portions and, with a fish slice, carefully lift out the squares on to warmed serving plates.

Pork with red cabbage

18 Points per recipe | **Takes 20 minutes to prepare, 1¼ hours to cook**

Serves 4. Calories per serving 340. Freeze ✓

The deep red colour will seep out of the cabbage as it cooks, giving the dish a wonderfully rich appearance.

700 g (1 lb 9 oz) boneless pork loin	1 tablespoon clear honey
1 teaspoon sunflower oil	1 teaspoon caraway seeds
450 g (1 lb) red cabbage, shredded	100 ml (3½ fl oz) red wine
2 red onions, sliced	300 ml (10 fl oz) pork stock
1 tablespoon balsamic vinegar	salt and freshly ground black pepper

1. Rinse the pork and pat it dry. With a piece of kitchen paper, wipe a large flameproof casserole dish with the oil. Heat the pan and add the pork and cook over a high heat on all sides, to brown and seal.

2. Lift the pork out of the pan and set aside. Add the remaining ingredients to the pan. Stir well and bring to the boil.

3. Replace the pork and cover. Reduce the heat and simmer for 1 hour.

4. Remove the lid of the dish and simmer, uncovered, for a further 15 minutes, so that some of the liquid evaporates.

5. Lift the pork out on to a serving platter and spoon the red cabbage mixture around the edge. Serve on four warmed plates, allowing 125 g (4½ oz) of pork per person.

Thai beef curry

22 Points per recipe | Takes 40 minutes

Serves 4. Calories per serving 275. Freeze ✓
This spicy little number is a fantastic winter warmer.

300 ml (10 fl oz) 88% fat free coconut milk	450 g (1 lb) lean rump steak, trimmed of
2 tablespoons Thai red curry paste	any fat and sliced thinly
1 stalk of lemongrass, sliced thinly	225 g (8 oz) shallots
4 dried or fresh kaffir lime leaves	150 g (5½ oz) carrots, sliced thinly
1 tablespoon fresh lime juice	175 g (6 oz) sugar snap peas
1 tablespoon Thai fish sauce	175 g (6 oz) cherry tomatoes, halved
	3 tablespoons chopped fresh coriander

1. Place the coconut milk in a large saucepan with 300 ml (10 fl oz) of water. Add the curry paste, lemongrass, kaffir lime leaves, lime juice and fish sauce, and bring to the boil. Boil rapidly for 2 minutes.

2. Add the steak and shallots to the pan, and simmer for 10 minutes. Add the carrots and sugar snap peas and cook for a further 10 minutes

3. Stir in the cherry tomatoes and chopped coriander and heat them through for 2 minutes. Serve the curry ladled into warmed bowls.

tip: *Adding the meat to the boiling liquid is the traditional way curries are cooked in Thailand. You don't need to use any oil to fry and seal the meat, and with this method it becomes beautifully tender.*

goes well with...

4 tablespoons of cooked rice for an extra 3 Points.

Sweet and sour pork meatballs

16½ Points per recipe | Takes 45 minutes

Serves 4. Calories per serving 280. Freeze ✓

450 g (1 lb) pork mince

1 small onion, chopped finely

1 garlic clove, crushed

low fat cooking spray

1 red pepper, de-seeded and diced

1 green pepper, de-seeded and diced

125 g (4½ oz) mange tout peas

350 g (12 oz) tomatoes, quartered

125 g (4½ oz) canned pineapple chunks
  in natural juice, drained

100 ml (3½ fl oz) pineapple juice

2 tablespoons soy sauce

2 tablespoons tomato purée

1 tablespoon white wine vinegar

1 teaspoon cornflour

1. Place the mince in a mixing bowl, and add the onion and garlic. Using clean hands, mix well and shape the mixture into about 20 small meatballs.

2. Heat a large non stick frying pan and spray with low fat cooking spray. Quickly stir fry the meatballs, a few at a time, to seal them all over. Using a slotted spoon, remove them from the pan, and set aside.

3. Add the peppers, mange tout peas and tomatoes to the pan and stir fry for 5 minutes. Stir in the pineapple chunks and pineapple juice, soy sauce, tomato purée and vinegar, and bring to the boil. Return the meatballs to the pan, then reduce the heat, cover and simmer for 10 minutes.

4. Mix the cornflour with a little cold water to make a thin paste. Mix this into the pan and cook, stirring, until the sauce thickens a little. Serve on four warmed plates, allowing 5 meatballs per person.

try this: Add other zero Point vegetables to the stir fry, such as baby sweetcorn, baby carrots or fine green beans.

Grilled pork steaks with apple mash

19 Points per recipe | Takes 45 minutes + 20 minutes marinating

Serves 4. Calories per serving 350. Freeze ✓

The apple in the mashed potatoes gives it a hint of sweetness that tastes wonderful with the pork.

4 x 125 g (4½ oz) boneless pork loin steaks

2 teaspoons clear honey

1 garlic clove, crushed

2 tablespoons soy sauce

1 tablespoon tomato purée

450 g (1 lb) potatoes, peeled and diced

225 g (8 oz) cooking apple, peeled, cored
  and diced

25 g (1 oz) low fat spread

6 spring onions, sliced

salt and freshly ground black pepper

1. Score a criss cross pattern along the top of each pork steak and place them in a shallow dish. Mix together the honey, garlic, soy sauce and tomato purée and brush this mixture over the steaks. Cover and leave to marinate for 20 minutes.

2. Meanwhile, cook the potatoes in lightly salted, boiling water for 15 minutes, and then add the apple to the pan. Cook for a further 5 minutes. Drain well and mash the apple and potatoes together. Season to taste.

3. Grill the pork steaks under a medium to low heat for 5 minutes on each side.

4. Melt the low fat spread in a small saucepan and add the spring onions. Cook for 2 minutes to soften them, and then spoon them into the mash and mix well.

5. Divide the mash between four serving plates and top with a cooked pork steak.

Chinese special pork rice

17½ Points per recipe | Takes 1 hour + 1 hour marinating

Serves 4. Calories per serving 535. Freeze ✓

A great Saturday night supper dish.

350 g (12 oz) pork tenderloin	low fat cooking spray
1 tablespoon Chinese five spice powder	150 g (5½ oz) carrots, diced finely
2 tablespoons soy sauce	100 g (3½ oz) frozen peas
2 tablespoons tomato ketchup	6 spring onions, sliced
350 g (12 oz) long grain white rice, cooked and cooled	150 g (5½ oz) fresh beansprouts
	1 egg, beaten

1. Rinse the pork and pat it dry with kitchen paper. Place it in a dish. Mix together the five spice powder, soy sauce and tomato ketchup, and spoon it over the pork. Leave the pork to marinate for 1 hour.

2. Preheat the oven to Gas Mark 6/200°C/fan oven 180°C. Place the marinated pork in a roasting tin and roast for 40 minutes.

3. While the pork is cooking, using clean hands, gently separate the cooked, cooled rice grains. Heat a large non stick frying pan and spray it with low fat cooking spray. Add the carrots, peas, spring onions and beansprouts, and stir fry for 2–3 minutes. Mix the rice into the pan and cook, stirring frequently, for 5 minutes.

4. Push the rice mixture to one side of the pan and pour the egg in the cleared space. Cook, without stirring, until you see the egg setting and then mix the cooked egg into the rice.

5. Using two forks, shred the cooked pork and mix it into the rice. Serve hot.

Bangers and parsley mash with red onion gravy

14 Points per recipe | Takes 25 minutes to prepare, 15 minutes to cook

Serves 2. Calories per serving 425. Freeze ✓

1 teaspoon sunflower oil	salt and freshly ground black pepper
4 x 50 g (1¾ oz) low fat sausages	For the mash:
1 red onion, sliced	350 g (12 oz) potatoes, peeled and diced
300 ml (10 fl oz) beef stock	15 g (½ oz) low fat spread
2 tablespoons port	2 tablespoons chopped fresh parsley
½ teaspoon Dijon mustard	2 tablespoons skimmed milk
1 tablespoon cornflour	salt and freshly ground black pepper

1. Heat the oil in a non stick frying pan and add the sausages and onion. Cook over a medium to low heat for 10 minutes, until the onion has softened and the sausages have turned brown.

2. Add the stock, port, mustard and seasoning to the pan, and bring to the boil. Reduce the heat and simmer for 15 minutes.

3. Make the mash: cook the potatoes in lightly salted, boiling water for 12–15 minutes until tender. Drain and mash them with the low fat spread, parsley, milk and seasoning.

4. Mix the cornflour with 2 tablespoons of cold water to make a thin paste, and then stir into the frying pan. Cook until the gravy thickens a little.

5. Divide the mash between two warmed plates and top with two sausages and the onion gravy.

7 POINTS

Sticky pineapple and mustard gammon steaks

28 Points per recipe | Takes 20 minutes

Serves 4. Calories per serving 355. Freeze ✓

Gammon tends to be quite high in Points, so serve these delicious steaks with a selection of zero Point vegetables.

4 x 175 g (6 oz) gammon steaks

200 g (7 oz) canned pineapple chunks in
    natural juice, drained and chopped
    roughly

1 tablespoon wholegrain mustard

1 tablespoon clear honey

1 tablespoon dark soy sauce

25 g (1 oz) fresh white breadcrumbs

1. Place the gammon steaks under a hot grill and cook for 2 minutes on each side.

2. Mix the pineapple with the mustard, honey, soy sauce and breadcrumbs. Spread this mixture evenly over one side of each gammon steak. Return the steaks to the grill and cook under a low heat for 5–7 minutes, until the topping is golden and bubbling.

tip: *If you snip the gammon at 2.5 cm (1 inch) intervals around the edges, it will prevent it from curling as you grill it.*

goes well with...

200 g (7 oz) boiled new potatoes, for an extra 2 Points.

Sticky sesame pork kebabs

28½ Points per recipe | Takes 30 minutes + 15 minutes marinating

Serves 4. Calories per serving 515. Freeze ✓

Adding herbs and lime zest to the plain boiled rice in this dish, helps to liven it up without adding any extra Points.

450 g (1 lb) pork tenderloin, trimmed of any fat and cut into bite sized cubes	2 tablespoons dark soy sauce
1 garlic clove, crushed	2 tablespoons sherry
2.5 cm (1 inch) piece of root ginger, peeled and grated	2 teaspoons sesame oil
	300 g (10½ oz) white long grain rice
1 fresh red chilli, de-seeded and chopped finely	a pinch of salt
	2 tablespoons chopped fresh coriander
	finely grated zest of 1 lime
1 tablespoon clear honey	1 tablespoon sesame seeds, toasted, to serve

1. Place the pork in a dish with the garlic, ginger, chilli, honey, soy sauce, sherry and sesame oil. Mix together well, cover and leave to marinate for 15 minutes.

2. Thread the pork cubes on to eight wooden skewers and grill for 12–15 minutes under a medium to low heat, turning frequently.

3. Meanwhile, put the rice in a large saucepan with 400 ml (14 fl oz) of water and a pinch of salt. Bring to the boil, and then reduce the heat, cover, and simmer without stirring for 12 minutes. Remove the pan from the heat. Fluff up the grains with a fork and mix in the coriander and lime zest.

4. To serve, divide the rice between four warmed plates. Top each with two kebabs and scatter with sesame seeds.

tip: *Soak wooden skewers for 30 minutes in a shallow bowl of water. This will prevent them burning under the grill.*

try this: Ⓥ *For a vegetarian version, use Quorn pieces instead of pork. This will reduce the Points to 6½ per serving.*

Traditional roast pork

16½ Points per recipe | Takes 20 minutes to prepare, 1 hour to cook

Serves 4. Calories per serving 240. Freeze ✓

Tasty as it may be, it's best to cut off all the crackling as this will make the Points soar; remove it before carving then you won't be tempted to have a nibble.

600 g (1 lb 5 oz) boneless pork loin	50 g (1¾ oz) ready to eat dried apricots, chopped finely
For the stuffing:	
2 teaspoons olive oil	25 g (1 oz) fresh white breadcrumbs
1 small onion, chopped finely	2 tablespoons fresh orange juice
100 g (3½ oz) mushrooms, sliced	salt and freshly ground black pepper
1 teaspoon dried thyme	

1. Preheat the oven to Gas Mark 5 /190°C/fan oven 170°C. Rinse the pork loin and pat it dry with kitchen paper.

2. To make the stuffing, heat the oil in a small pan and add the onion and mushrooms. Cook, stirring, over a medium to low heat for 5 minutes until the onion softens but does not brown. Add the thyme, apricots and breadcrumbs, and cook for 1 minute. Remove from the heat and stir in the orange juice.

3. Open out the pork loin and press the stuffing into the cavity. Use string to tie the pork up, fastening it tightly.

4. Place the pork in a roasting tin, season well with salt and freshly ground black pepper, and roast for 1 hour. Allow it to rest a while before carving it into slices and dividing the meat between four plates.

Mustard pork on crushed potatoes

22 Points per recipe | Takes 40 minutes

Serves 4. Calories per serving 380. Freeze ✓

Lightly crushing the potatoes rather than mashing them gives the dish a different texture and it looks good too!

2 teaspoons sunflower oil

4 x 150 g (5½ oz) boneless pork loin steaks

150 ml (5 fl oz) cider

1 tablespoon wholegrain mustard

1 pork stock cube, crumbled

450 g (1 lb) baby new potatoes, scrubbed

15 g (½ oz) polyunsaturated margarine

1 tablespoon finely chopped fresh chives

salt and freshly ground black pepper

1. Heat the sunflower oil in a non stick frying pan and add the pork steaks. Cook them over a medium heat for 2–3 minutes until browned. Add the cider, mustard and stock cube to the pan, stir well and bring to the boil. Reduce the heat, cover and simmer over a low heat for 30 minutes.

2. Meanwhile, cook the potatoes in lightly salted, boiling water for 15 minutes, until they are tender. Drain well and, using a potato masher, lightly crush them.

3. Heat the margarine in a frying pan and add the crushed potatoes and chives. Mix well and heat through. Season with freshly ground black pepper.

4. To serve, divide the crushed potatoes between four warmed serving plates and top with a pork steak and a generous drizzle of the cooking juices.

Pork casserole with chive dumplings

20½ Points per recipe | Takes 25 minutes to prepare, 1¼ hours to cook

Serves 4. Calories per serving 415. Freeze ✓

low fat cooking spray

450 g (1 lb) pork tenderloin, cubed

2 red onions, cut into wedges

225 g (8 oz) carrots, sliced

225 g (8 oz) swede, cubed

600 ml (20 fl oz) pork stock

1 teaspoon dried sage

1 tablespoon Worcestershire sauce

salt and freshly ground black pepper

For the dumplings:

175 g (6 oz) self raising white flour

1 teaspoon baking powder

a pinch of salt

2 tablespoons finely chopped fresh chives

1 tablespoon olive oil

1. Heat a large, flameproof casserole dish and spray it with low fat cooking spray. Add the pork and cook, stirring, for 5 minutes to seal the meat. Add the onions, carrots and swede to the pan, and stir well.

2. Pour over the stock and add the sage, Worcestershire sauce and seasoning. Bring to the boil, reduce the heat, cover and simmer for 40 minutes.

3. Meanwhile, in a mixing bowl, sift the flour with the baking powder and a pinch of salt. Stir in the chives and olive oil, and then add enough 'hand hot' water to mix to a soft dough. Divide the mixture into eight small balls and arrange them around the edge of the casserole.

4. Cover and simmer for a further 20–25 minutes, until the dumplings have risen and are firm to the touch. Serve on four warmed plates, allowing two dumplings per person.

try this: *If you don't have fresh chives for the dumplings, use a teaspoon of dried mixed herbs or a teaspoon of wholegrain mustard instead.*

Toad in the hole

24 Points per recipe | Takes 20 minutes to prepare, 45 minutes to cook

Serves 4. Calories per serving 375. Freeze ✗

The vegetables in this popular dish add a burst of colour. They also make it a more filling meal without adding any Points!

	For the batter:
1 tablespoon sunflower oil	**100 g (3½ oz) plain white flour**
450 g (1 lb) low fat pork sausages	**a pinch of salt**
225 g (8 oz) carrots, cut into thick chunks	**1 egg**
1 red onion, cut into wedges	**300 ml (10 fl oz) skimmed milk**
4 celery sticks, cut into 5 cm (2 inch)	**1 teaspoon dried mixed herbs**
pieces	

1. Preheat the oven to Gas Mark 6/200°C/fan oven 180°C. Place the oil in a 23 cm (9 inch) square non stick baking tin. Arrange the sausages, carrots, onion and celery in the base of the tin. Roast in the oven for 20 minutes.
2. Meanwhile, make the batter. Sift the flour and salt into a mixing bowl, and make a well in the centre. Add the egg, milk and herbs and whisk to form a smooth batter.
3. Remove the sausages and vegetables from the oven and pour over the batter. Return the tin to the oven for 20–25 minutes, until the batter is well risen and deep golden.
4. Cut the toad in the hole into quarters and serve hot.

try this: *Try using other zero Point vegetables for this dish, such as open cup mushrooms or chunks of leeks or courgettes.*

All in one breakfast omelette

5 Points per recipe | Takes 30 minutes

Serves 1. Calories per serving 315. Freeze ✗

This is a delicious and healthy breakfast; it's a great kickstart to the day!

25 g (1 oz) lean back bacon rasher	**2 eggs**
1 teaspoon sunflower oil	**2 tablespoons skimmed milk**
100 g (3½ oz) mushrooms, sliced	**salt and freshly ground black pepper**
1 tomato, sliced	

1. Preheat the grill to a medium heat. Grill the bacon until it is crispy. Cut it into strips.
2. Heat the sunflower oil in a small non stick frying pan and add the mushrooms. Cook for 5 minutes, until they are softened and then add the tomato slices. Cook for a further 2 minutes. Remove them from the pan and set aside.
3. Whisk the eggs with the milk and seasoning and pour this into the pan. Cook for 2–3 minutes until you see the edges of the egg setting. Using a wooden spatula, draw the cooked egg into the centre of the pan, allowing the runny, uncooked egg to run to the edges.
4. When the egg is nearly set, arrange the cooked mushrooms, tomato and strips of grilled bacon on one side of the omelette. Using a spatula, flip the clear half of the omelette over the filling. Carefully slide it on to a warmed serving plate and eat at once.

try this: **Ⓥ** *For a vegetarian option, make sure you use free-range eggs and use a soya bacon rasher instead. Soya bacon rashers are readily available in supermarkets, but remember to alter the Points accordingly.*

sweets...
and puddings

2 POINTS

Tiramisu

9 Points per recipe | **Takes 25 minutes + 1 hour chilling**

V *Serves 4. Calories per serving 260. Freeze ✓*

This is a delicious low Point version of the famous Italian dessert.

---

8 sponge fingers

1 tablespoon coffee granules

3 tablespoons boiling water

1 tablespoon granulated artificial sweetener

3 tablespoons Marsala wine

350 ml (12 fl oz) 0% fat Greek style plain yogurt

1 egg white

25 g (1 oz) plain chocolate with 70% cocoa solids, grated, to serve

---

1. Divide the sponge fingers between four individual shallow glass dishes.

2. Dissolve the coffee granules in the boiling water, and stir in the sweetener and Marsala wine. Drizzle the coffee mixture equally over the sponge fingers.

3. Place the yogurt in a mixing bowl. Whisk the egg white until it forms soft peaks and fold it into the yogurt. Spoon this over the soaked sponge fingers.

4. Cover and chill the dishes for at least 1 hour or overnight. Sprinkle the top of each tiramisù with grated chocolate, and serve.

try this: *For a lemon version of this recipe, replace the coffee granules and water with 3 tablespoons of freshly squeezed lemon juice. Sprinkle the tops with finely grated lemon or orange zest.*

If you can't find any Marsala wine use some brandy instead. The Points will be 2$^{1}/_{2}$ per serving.

Blackberry and apple filo pies

9 Points per recipe | **Takes 30 minutes to prepare, 15 minutes to bake**

V *Serves 6. Calories per serving 120. Freeze* ✔

These little crisp pastries filled with juicy fruits are a delicious after dinner low Point treat.

350 g (12 oz) cooking apples, peeled, cored and diced	1 tablespoon cornflour
15 g (½ oz) granulated artificial sweetener	6 sheets filo pastry
a pinch of ground nutmeg	15 g (½ oz) polyunsaturated margarine, melted
225 g (8 oz) blackberries	

1. Line a baking tray with non stick baking parchment.

2. Place the apples in a small saucepan with 3 tablespoons of water, the sweetener and nutmeg. Cover and simmer gently for 5 minutes until the apple begins to soften.

3. Stir in the blackberries and cook for a further 2 minutes. Mix the cornflour with 2 tablespoons of cold water to make a thin paste and stir this into the fruit. Cook, stirring, until the mixture thickens. Remove the pan from the heat and allow to cool.

4. Preheat the oven to Gas Mark 5/190°C/fan oven 170°C. Brush a filo pastry sheet with a little melted margarine and fold it in half. Spoon some of the cooled apple and blackberry mixture into the centre of the folded sheet. Now gather up the edges of the pastry and twist them, to seal it like a purse. Repeat the process with the remaining pastry sheets and then brush the pastry purses with any remaining melted margarine.

5. Bake for 12–15 minutes, until the pastry is golden and crisp.

Creamy rice pudding with apricot purée

12½ Points per recipe | **Takes 15 minutes to prepare, 1 hour to cook**

Serves 6. Calories per serving 155. Freeze ✗

Eaten hot or cold, this creamy rice dish is always delicious.

100 g (3½ oz) pudding rice	25 g (1 oz) caster sugar
600 ml (20 fl oz) skimmed milk	100 g (3½ oz) ready to eat dried apricots, chopped
1 teaspoon vanilla essence	300 ml (10 fl oz) fresh orange juice
a pinch of ground nutmeg	

1. Place the pudding rice in a medium saucepan with the milk, vanilla essence, nutmeg and caster sugar, and bring it to the boil. Reduce the heat to very low, cover and simmer for 1 hour, stirring from time to time, until the rice is tender and the mixture is creamy.

2. Meanwhile, place the apricots in a small saucepan with the orange juice, and simmer gently for 15 minutes. Allow the mixture to cool for 10 minutes and then purée in a food processor or liquidiser.

3. Divide the rice pudding between six small dishes and drizzle the apricot purée over the top.

try this: *As a change, try stirring in 50 g (1¾ oz) of sultanas to the rice mixture for the last 10 minutes of cooking; this will add ½ a Point per serving. For a citrus tang, mix in a teaspoon of orange zest, but if you are adding this leave out the vanilla essence.*

Chocolate orange mousse

9 Points per recipe | Takes 20 minutes + 2 hours chilling

V *Serves 4. Calories per serving 130. Freeze ✗*

Calling all chocoholics! This is one way to get your fix without using too many precious Points.

---

25 g (1 oz) plain chocolate with 70% cocoa
   solids

300 ml (10 fl oz) low fat plain fromage frais

1 sachet low fat hot chocolate orange drink
   (e.g. Options)

2 tablespoons boiling water

finely grated zest of 1 orange plus extra
   for decoration

1 egg white

---

1. Break the chocolate into small squares. Place the squares in a small bowl over a pan of simmering water until the chocolate has melted. Allow it to cool a little.

2. Place the fromage frais in a bowl and beat the cooled chocolate into it.

3. Mix the chocolate orange drink with the boiling water to make a thick paste. Beat this into the fromage frais and chocolate mixture, and then add the orange zest.

4. Whisk the egg white until it forms soft peaks and fold it into the chocolate mixture. Divide the mixture between four individual ramekin dishes and chill for 2 hours or overnight.

5. Serve decorated with a little orange zest sprinkled on top of each one.

Ginger and orange cheesecake

36½ Points per recipe | Takes 15 minutes + 20 minutes cooling + 4½ hours chilling

V *Serves 8. Calories per serving 240. Freeze ✓*

The spicy tang of the ginger together with the slight sharpness of the orange makes this a winning combination.

For the base:

150 g (5½ oz) reduced fat digestive biscuits,
   crushed

75 g (2¾ oz) polyunsaturated margarine,
   melted

1 teaspoon finely grated orange zest

For the filling:

200 ml (7 fl oz) boiling water

1 sachet sugar free orange flavour jelly

300 g (10½ oz) low fat soft cheese

50 g (1¾ oz) caster sugar

150 ml (5 fl oz) 0% fat Greek style plain
   yogurt

50 g (1¾ oz) stem ginger, drained and
   chopped finely

2 oranges, peeled and segmented

---

1. Mix together the crushed biscuits, melted margarine and orange zest. Press the mixture into the base of a round, loose bottomed non stick 20 cm (8 inch) cake tin. Chill in the fridge while preparing the filling.

2. Pour the boiling water over the jelly crystals and stir well. Allow to cool for 20 minutes, and then whisk in the low fat soft cheese, caster sugar, yogurt and stem ginger. Chill the mixture in the refrigerator for 30 minutes.

3. Spoon the cheese mixture over the base. Return to the fridge for at least 4 hours until completely set.

4. Carefully remove the cheesecake from the tin and place it on a serving plate. Decorate the top with orange segments. Cut into eight wedges to serve.

try this: *You can use a 215 g can of mandarin oranges in natural juice to decorate the top if you prefer. The Points will remain the same.*

Strawberry syllabub

5 Points per recipe | Takes 15 minutes + 30 minutes chilling

V *Serves 2. Calories per serving 80. Freeze ✓ (see tip)*

In the summer months, when fresh strawberries are in abundance, make the most of them as they are both delicious and low in Points.

---

175 g (6 oz) fresh strawberries, hulled
   and sliced

1 tablespoon granulated artificial sweetener

1 tablespoon port

175 ml (6 fl oz) low fat strawberry
   fromage frais

---

1. Reserve 1 strawberry and place the remaining strawberries in a food processor with the sweetener and port. Blend until smooth.

2. Place the fromage frais in a mixing bowl and stir in the strawberry purée.

3. Divide the syllabub mixture between two small dishes and chill for 30 minutes. Decorate each one with slices of the reserved strawberry before serving.

tip: *You can freeze this mixture to make a superb ice cream. Take it out of the freezer 20 minutes before serving.*

goes well with...

two amaretti biscuits for 1 extra Point.

Melon, kiwi and raspberry fruit salad

4 Points per recipe | **Takes 15 minutes**

V **Vg** *Serves 4. Calories 65. Freeze* ✗

The jewel like colours of this fruit salad lets you know you're in for a real treat.

---

450 g (1 lb) honeydew melon, de-seeded,
   peeled and diced

2 kiwi fruit, sliced thinly

350 g (12 oz) fresh or frozen raspberries

2 tablespoons artificial granulated
   sweetener

4 sprigs of fresh mint, to decorate

---

1. Mix together the diced melon and kiwi slices, and divide them between four individual glasses.

2. Push the raspberries through a sieve to purée them, discard the seeds and stir the artificial sweetener into the purée.

3. Drizzle the raspberry purée over the melon and kiwi fruit, and decorate each one with a sprig of mint.

tip: *Frozen raspberries are good for puréeing because they give out more juice than fresh raspberries.*

Sticky toffee pudding

21 Points per recipe | **Takes 20 minutes to prepare, 40 minutes to cook**

V *Serves 4. Calories per serving 320. Freeze* ✓

For all those with a sweet tooth, this is the pudding for you! High in satisfaction but low in Points!

---

low fat cooking spray

50 g (1¾ oz) polyunsaturated margarine

50 g (1¾ oz) dark soft brown sugar

2 eggs, beaten

100 g (3½ oz) self raising white flour

2 tablespoons boiling water

3 tablespoons golden syrup

---

1. Spray four individual metal moulds with a little low fat cooking spray.

2. Place the margarine and sugar in a warmed mixing bowl and beat them together until fluffy. Beat in the eggs and then fold in the flour with the boiling water.

3. Divide the golden syrup between the four moulds and then spoon the sponge mixture over the top.

4. Transfer the moulds to a steamer and steam for 40 minutes. Take care never to allow the steamer to boil dry, top up with boiling water if necessary.

5. To serve, carefully run a round bladed knife around the edge of the moulds and turn them out on to four small serving plates.

try this: *Serve each pudding with 3 tablespoons of low fat custard. The Points per serving will be increased to 6.*

tip: *If you don't own a steamer, simply place an upturned saucer in the base of a medium saucepan and add the moulds. Pour a little water around the moulds and then place the pan, covered, on the hob and steam for the same time.*

Baked chocolate custard pots

14½ Points per recipe | Takes 20 minutes to prepare, 1 hour to bake + 2 hours chilling

V *Serves 4. Calories per serving 205. Freeze* ✓

2 eggs plus 1 egg yolk	25 g (1 oz) cocoa powder
300 ml (10 fl oz) skimmed milk	25 g (1 oz) caster sugar
50 g (1¾ oz) plain chocolate with 70% cocoa solids	

1. Preheat the oven to Gas Mark 2/150°C/fan oven 130°C. Half fill a roasting tin with boiling water.

2. Place the eggs and egg yolk in a bowl with the milk and beat well. Strain the mixture into a clean saucepan and heat very gently – do not boil, it just needs to get warm. Remove from the heat.

3. Grate the chocolate over the egg mixture and sift in the cocoa powder. Add the sugar and whisk well.

4. Pour the chocolate mixture into four individual ramekin dishes. Place the dishes in the roasting tin. Bake in the oven for 1 hour, until the custards have set.

5. Allow to cool and then chill for 2 hours.

tip: *Cooking delicate dishes in a water bath, known as a bain marie, spreads the heat, so they cook slowly for a more velvety texture and prevents them from curdling.*

Chocolate puddings with chocolate sauce

14 Points per recipe | Takes 25 minutes to prepare, 15 minutes to bake + 20 minutes cooling

V *Serves 4. Calories per serving 210. Freeze* ✗

low fat cooking spray	For the sauce:
2 eggs	1 sachet low fat chocolate drink
50 g (1¾ oz) caster sugar	(e.g. High Lights)
75 g (2¾ oz) plain flour	300 ml (10 fl oz) boiling water
25 g (1 oz) cocoa powder	1 tablespoon cornflour
2 drops vanilla essence	3 tablespoons chocolate flavour low fat
1 tablespoon skimmed milk	yogurt (e.g. Müller Light)

1. Lightly spray four individual ramekin dishes or dariole moulds with low fat cooking spray and line the base of each with a circle of non stick baking parchment. Preheat the oven to Gas Mark 4/180°C/fan oven 160°C.

2. Place the eggs and caster sugar in a mixing bowl. Using electric beaters, whisk until the mixture becomes fluffy and pale in colour.

3. Sift the flour and cocoa powder into the egg mixture, folding it in with a metal spoon along with the vanilla essence and milk. Divide the pudding mixture between the lined ramekin dishes or dariole moulds. Bake for 15 minutes, until the sponges are firm and springy to the touch.

4. To make the sauce, place the sachet of chocolate drink in a medium saucepan with the water and cornflour. Cook, whisking, until the sauce is slightly thickened. Remove the pan from the heat, allow the mixture to cool for about 20 minutes and then whisk in the yogurt.

5. Run a round bladed knife around the edge of each pudding. Turn them out on to four serving plates. Drizzle the chocolate sauce over the puddings and serve them warm.

try this: *Fold some finely grated orange zest into the pudding mixture in step 3, to add a citrus tang.*

Lime meringue tart

27½ Points per recipe | Takes 1 hour + 20 minutes chilling

v *Serves 6. Calories per serving 275. Freeze* ✗

This classic tart is traditionally made with lemons, but this lime version gives this old favourite a new lease of life!

For the pastry:
125 g (4½ oz) plain white flour, plus
   2 teaspoons for rolling
25 g (1 oz) cornflour
a pinch of salt
75 g (2¾ oz) polyunsaturated margarine

For the filling:
3 tablespoons cornflour
finely grated zest and juice of 3 limes
15 g (½ oz) granulated artificial sweetener
2 egg yolks
For the meringue:
2 egg whites
50 g (1¾ oz) caster sugar

1. To make the pastry, sift the flour and cornflour along with the salt into a mixing bowl. Rub in the margarine with your fingertips until the mixture resembles fine breadcrumbs. Add enough cold water to mix to a soft dough.
2. Roll out the pastry on a lightly floured surface and use it to line a 20 cm (8 inch) loose bottomed fluted flan tin. Chill the pastry in the fridge for 20 minutes.
3. Preheat the oven to Gas Mark 6/200°C/fan oven 180°C. Line the pastry case with non stick baking parchment and baking beans and bake blind for 10 minutes. Remove the beans and lining paper and return it to the oven for 10 minutes, until the pastry is pale golden and crisp.
4. Meanwhile, make the filling. Whisk together the cornflour, 150 ml (5 fl oz) of water, lime zest and lime juice, artificial sweetener and egg yolks. Heat the mixture gently in a small saucepan over a low heat, stirring continuously, until you have a thick sauce.
5. Spoon the filling into the cooked pastry case and level it with the back of a spoon.
6. To make the meringue, place the egg whites in a clean mixing bowl and whisk them with electric beaters until stiff. Add the sugar a spoonful at a time and continue whisking until you have a thick, glossy meringue mixture.
7. Spoon the meringue over the lime filling, using the back of a spoon to swirl it over the top. Return the tart to the oven for 5–8 minutes, until the meringue is golden brown and crisp on top.

tip: *When baking a pastry case, line it with non stick baking parchment and baking beans. Otherwise the pastry shrinks as it cooks. If you don't have baking beans use dried pulses, such as kidney beans or marrowfat peas.*

Baked nectarines with ricotta and amaretti biscuits

6½ Points per recipe | Takes 15 minutes to prepare, 15 minutes to bake

v *Serves 2. Calories per serving 205. Freeze* ✓

2 nectarines, halved and stoned
50 g (1¾ oz) ricotta cheese
1 teaspoon clear honey

25 g (1 oz) amaretti biscuits, crushed
1 tablespoon amaretto liqueur

1. Preheat the oven to Gas Mark 4/180°C/fan oven 160°C. Place the nectarines, cut halves facing up, on a baking tray.
2. Beat together the ricotta cheese, honey, Amaretti biscuits and Amaretto liqueur.
3. Spoon the cheese mixture on top of the nectarine halves, pressing down slightly. Bake the nectarines for 15 minutes. Serve hot.

tip: *Cut a small slice off the base of each nectarine to stop them wobbling on the baking tray.*

Chocolate ginger roulade

12½ Points per recipe | Takes 40 minutes + 1 hour cooling

V *Makes 8 slices. Calories per serving 120. Freeze ✓*

The richness of chocolate with the spicy tang of ginger makes a heavenly combination.

150 ml (5 fl oz) skimmed milk	25 g (1 oz) stem ginger, chopped finely
25 g (1 oz) cornflour	1 sachet low fat hot chocolate drink
25 g (1 oz) cocoa powder	(e.g. High Lights)
50 g (1¾ oz) caster sugar	1 tablespoon boiling water
3 eggs, separated	1 teaspoon icing sugar, for dusting
150 ml (5 fl oz) low fat plain fromage frais	

1. Preheat the oven to Gas Mark 6/200°C/fan oven 180°C. Line a 19 cm x 28 cm (7½ inch x 11 inch) Swiss roll tin with non stick baking parchment.

2. In a medium saucepan, whisk together the milk, cornflour, cocoa powder and caster sugar. Gently heat the mixture, stirring constantly, until you have a very thick sauce. Remove the pan from the heat and transfer the sauce to a mixing bowl.

3. Beat the egg yolks into the chocolate mixture. Using electric beaters, whisk the egg whites into soft peaks and then fold them into the mixture with a metal spoon.

4. Transfer the mixture to the lined Swiss roll tin – shake the tin gently to spread it out evenly – and bake in the oven for 12 minutes.

5. Turn out the sponge on to a clean sheet of non stick baking parchment. Peel away the lining paper. Using the clean sheet as a guide, carefully roll up the roulade. Allow it to cool for 1 hour.

6. In a bowl, mix the fromage frais with the ginger. Mix the low fat hot chocolate drink with the boiling water to make a thick paste and fold this into the fromage frais and ginger mixture.

7. Carefully unroll the cooled roulade, and spread the chocolate and ginger filling over it. Re-roll the roulade and then place it on a serving plate. Dust the top with icing sugar.

tip: *Don't worry if the surface of the roulade cracks a little. This is normal and gives the roulade its character.*

Pineapple custard

3½ Points per recipe | Takes 15 minutes

V *Serves 1. Calories per serving 280. Freeze ✗*

This easy and quick recipe is just the thing when you fancy a low Point treat just for yourself.

2 sponge fingers, crumbed	125 g tub of low fat custard
¼ of 227 g can of pineapple chunks in natural juice	

1. Place the sponge finger crumbs in the base of an individual dish.

2. Spoon the pineapple, reserving two chunks, and any juice over the crumbs. Leave the dish to stand for 5–10 minutes, so the juice becomes absorbed by the sponge.

3. Top with the custard and then decorate the top with the reserved pineapple. Chill in the fridge until required.

Home made vanilla ice cream

9 Points per recipe | Takes 35 minutes + 30 minutes cooling + 6 hours freezing + 20 minutes standing

Serves 6. Calories per serving 115. Freeze ✓

A delicious, velvety smooth ice cream for an irresistable, low Point treat.

600 ml (20 fl oz) skimmed milk	25 g (1 oz) caster sugar
1 vanilla pod, split	25 g (1 oz) cornflour
2 egg yolks	150 ml (5 fl oz) 0% fat Greek style plain yogurt

1. Heat the milk and vanilla pod in a medium pan until the milk is just boiling. Remove the pan from the heat and whisk in the egg yolks and caster sugar.

2. Using a sieve, strain the mixture into a clean non stick medium saucepan. Mix the cornflour with a little cold water to make a thin paste and add this to the pan. Cook, stirring continuously, until the custard mixture thickens. Cool, remove the vanilla pod, and then chill for 30 minutes

3. Whisk the yogurt into the chilled custard and transfer it to a freezer container, and freeze. After 2 hours remove it from the freezer and whisk well. Freeze for another 2 hours and then whisk again. Return it to the freezer until the ice cream is frozen solid.

4. About 20 minutes before serving, take the ice cream out of the freezer and let it stand before scooping it out.

tip: *When cooling custards, cover with a sheet of dampened greaseproof paper. This will prevent a skin from forming.*

Crêpes with banana and tropical rum liqueur

8 Points per recipe | Takes 40 minutes

Ⓥ *Serves 2. Calories per serving 305. Freeze* ✓ *(pancakes only)*

50 g (1¾ oz) plain white flour	1 banana
a pinch of salt	1 teaspoon polyunsaturated margarine
1 small egg	1 tablespoon dark brown soft sugar
150 ml (5 fl oz) skimmed milk	2 tablespoons tropical rum liqueur
low fat cooking spray	(e.g. Malibu)

1. Sift the flour into a mixing bowl with the salt. Add the egg and milk, and whisk to a smooth batter.

2. Spray a 20 cm (8 inch) non stick frying pan with a little low fat cooking spray and heat. Pour a little of the batter into the pan, swirling the pan to spread the mixture over the base. Cook for 1–2 minutes. Flip the pancake over and cook the other side for 1–2 minutes until golden in colour. Make four pancakes in this way.

3. Fold the pancakes into quarters. Peel and slice the banana.

4. Heat the margarine in a frying pan, and add the banana and sugar. Cook, stirring, for 2 minutes and then add the liqueur. Arrange the folded pancakes in the pan, warm the pancakes through and serve.

Summer berry pudding

13 Points per recipe | Takes 30 minutes + chilling overnight

V *Serves 6. Calories per serving 120. Freeze* ✓

A classic English pudding that makes an attractive centre piece at any dinner party.

8 medium slices of white bread, crusts removed	175 g (6 oz) strawberries, hulled and quartered
225 g (8 oz) raspberries	15 g (½ oz) granulated artificial sweetener
175 g (6 oz) redcurrants	2 tablespoons sugar free blackcurrant cordial
175 g (6 oz) blueberries	

1. Cut the bread to line the base and sides of a 700 ml (1¼ pint) pudding basin – you need to reserve a couple of slices to make a lid for the top of the pudding.
2. Place the fruit in a medium size saucepan with the sweetener, blackcurrant cordial and 2 tablespoons of water. Cook over a low heat for 5 minutes, stirring carefully, so as not to break up the fruit.
3. Reserve two spoonfuls of the fruit and its juice. Spoon the remaining fruit and the juice into the bread lined basin. Cut the remaining bread to form a lid, and place it over the fruit. Cover the basin with clingfilm and then place a saucer over the top of the basin and put a weight on it – a can of beans would do. Place the weighted pudding in the fridge overnight.
4. Remove the weight, saucer and clingfilm from the pudding. Carefully run a round bladed knife around the edge of the basin and turn the pudding out on to a serving plate. Spoon over the reserved fruit and juices. Serve in slices.

tip: *If you can, use bread that's 2–3 days old for this recipe, the juice will soak into it far better than into fresh bread.*

Baked lemon and sultana cheesecake

47 Points per recipe | Takes 25 minutes to prepare, 1¼ hours to bake + 2 hours cooling

V *Serves 8. Calories per serving 250. Freeze* ✓

This baked cheesecake is absolutely sensational with the sultanas adding a natural sweetness.

175 g (6 oz) reduced fat digestive biscuits, crushed	finely grated zest and juice of 2 lemons
75 g (2¾ oz) polyunsaturated margarine, melted	3 eggs
350 g (12 oz) low fat plain cottage cheese	150 ml (5 fl oz) half fat crème fraîche
50 g (1¾ oz) caster sugar	½ teaspoon ground cinnamon
	50 g (1¾ oz) sultanas
	1 teaspoon icing sugar

1. Mix the crushed biscuits with the margarine and press over the base of a 20 cm (8 inch) loose bottomed springform tin.
2. Preheat the oven to Gas Mark 3/160°C/fan oven 140°C.
3. Push the cottage cheese through a sieve and then beat in the caster sugar, lemon zest and juice, eggs, crème fraîche, cinnamon and sultanas.
4. Spoon the cheese mixture over the biscuit base and bake for 1¼ hours.
5. Open the oven door and allow the cheesecake to cool in the oven for about 2 hours.
6. Carefully remove the cheesecake from the tin and place it on a serving plate. Dust the top with the icing sugar.

tip: *Crush the biscuits by putting them in a polythene bag and bashing them with a rolling pin, alternatively use a food processor.*

3 POINTS

Mango maple yogurt ice

11 Points per recipe | Takes 20 minutes + 4-6 hours freezing

Ⓥ *Serves 4. Calories per serving 170. Freeze ✓*

This refreshing yogurt ice is guaranteed to cool you down on hot summer days.

---

450 g (1 lb) mangoes, peeled, stoned
    and sliced
3 tablespoons maple syrup

finely grated zest and juice of 1 lime
600 ml (20 fl oz) low fat plain yogurt

---

1. Place the sliced mangoes in a food processor with the maple syrup, lime zest and juice and yogurt. Blend for about 30 seconds, until the mixture is smooth.

2. Transfer the mixture to a freezer container with a tight fitting lid and freeze for 2 hours. Remove from the freezer and whisk well to break down the ice crystals. Freeze for another hour, and then whisk again.

3. Repeat this two or three times more before the mixture freezes completely.

tip: *The more times you can whisk this yogurt ice while it is freezing, the smoother it will be.*

Sunday lunch

Relax and enjoy three courses for Sunday lunch and only spend 9 Points.

Zero Point vegetable broth *page 8*, 1 serving ....0 Points

Roast chicken with lemon, garlic and thyme
    page 121, 1 serving ....6 Points
Zero Point vegetables ....0 Points

Mango maple yogurt ice *above*, 1 serving ....3 Points
(pictured left)

Total Points for meal ....**9 Points**

Peach and blueberry brûlée

6 Points per recipe | **Takes 20 minutes + 2 hours chilling**

Ⓥ *Serves 2. Calories per serving 190. Freeze ✗*

Break into the sweet, crunchy topping to find the creamy, fruity layer underneath.

---

1 ripe peach, peeled and sliced

125 g (4½ oz) blueberries

150 ml (5 fl oz) 0% fat Greek style
    plain yogurt

100 ml (3½ fl oz) low fat plain fromage frais

2 tablespoons demerara sugar

---

1. Divide the peach slices between two ramekin dishes. Scatter the blueberries over the top.
2. Beat together the yogurt and fromage frais and spread this evenly over the fruit. Sprinkle 1 tablespoon of sugar on the top of each dish. Place the dishes under a very hot grill for about 2 minutes, until the sugar melts and bubbles.
3. Cool and then chill in the fridge for 2 hours, so the sugar topping forms a crunchy layer.

tip: *It is important that you grill the brûlées under a very hot grill. If the grill is not hot enough, you'll find that the yogurt mixture will melt before the sugar caramelises.*

Rhubarb and raspberry ginger crisp

10½ Points per recipe | **Takes 25 minutes to prepare + 1 hour chilling**

Serves 6. Calories per serving 130. Freeze ✓

Rhubarb is a zero Point fruit and is delicious combined with raspberries.

---

450 g (1 lb) rhubarb, sliced

4 tablespoons reduced sugar raspberry jam

175 g (6 oz) fresh or frozen raspberries

25 g (1 oz) stem ginger, chopped finely

2 tablespoons granulated artificial
    sweetener

25 g (1 oz) polyunsaturated margarine

1 tablespoon clear honey

75 g (2¾ oz) cornflakes

---

1. Place the rhubarb in a medium saucepan with the jam and 4 tablespoons of water. Cover and simmer for 10 minutes, until the rhubarb softens.
2. Stir in the raspberries, ginger and sweetener. Remove from the heat and divide the mixture between six individual dishes.
3. Melt the margarine in a medium saucepan with the honey. Stir in the cornflakes and then spoon this mixture on top of the fruit. Cool and then chill in the fridge for 1 hour.

try this: *If you're not keen on ginger leave it out and add a pinch of ground cinnamon instead.*

Black cherry and cinnamon crumble

27 Points per recipe | Takes 25 minutes to prepare, 25 minutes to bake

V ✔ *Serves 4. Calories per serving 435. Freeze ✔*

This crumble made with cherries alongside the traditional apple gives this dish a unique flavour and texture.

350 g (12 oz) cooking apples, peeled, cored and diced	**For the crumble:**
	150 g (5½ oz) plain white flour
425 g (15 oz) canned cherries in juice, stoned	1 teaspoon ground cinnamon
	75 g (2¾ oz) polyunsaturated margarine
1 tablespoon arrowroot	50 g (1¾ oz) demerara sugar

1. Preheat the oven to Gas Mark 5/190°C/fan oven 170°C.

2. Place the apples in a large saucepan with the canned cherries and juice, and heat until just boiling.

3. Mix the arrowroot with a little cold water to make a thin paste and stir this into the pan. Cook, stirring, until the juices thicken slightly. Spoon the fruit mixture into an ovenproof dish.

4. Sift the flour and cinnamon into a mixing bowl. Rub in the margarine using your fingertips, until the mixture resembles fine breadcrumbs. Stir in the sugar and then scatter the crumble over the top of the fruit.

5. Bake for 25 minutes, until the crumble topping is crunchy and golden. Serve hot or cold.

tip: *Look out for a good low fat custard to serve with this, or better still make your own with custard powder, skimmed milk and granulated artificial sweetener. Don't forget to alter the Points accordingly.*

goes well with...

3 tablespoons of ready to serve low fat custard for 1 extra Point.

Creamy blackcurrant crunch

13 Points per recipe | Takes 20 minutes

Ⓥ *Serves 4. Calories per serving 140. Freeze* ✗

A crunchy sweet texture tops a layer of creamy fromage frais, which in turn hides a delicious layer of flavour packed blackcurrants.

---

300 g (10½ oz) canned blackcurrants
   in juice, drained
3 tablespoons reduced sugar
   blackcurrant jam

300 ml (10 fl oz) low fat plain fromage frais
50 g (1¾ oz) crunchy oat cereal
   (e.g. Jordan's Original Crunchy)
2 teaspoons clear honey

---

1. Place the blackcurrants and jam in a small saucepan over a low heat for 2–3 minutes, until the jam melts and coats the blackcurrants.

2. Divide the mixture between four individual glasses and top each one with a layer of fromage frais.

3. Crumble the crunchy oat cereal over the top of each one and then finally drizzle the surface with a little honey.

try this: *You can vary the fruit in this dish – try fresh raspberries mixed with reduced sugar raspberry jam or canned apricots mixed with reduced sugar apricot jam. Adjust the Points accordingly.*

Chocolate chip bread and butter pudding

22 Points per recipe | Takes 20 minutes to prepare, 35 minutes to bake + 5 minutes standing

Ⓥ *Serves 4. Calories per serving 320. Freeze* ✓

Dig your spoon into this delightful pudding and you'll find little melting chunks of chocolate chips – delicious!

---

5 medium slices of white bread, crusts
   removed
15 g (½ oz) low fat spread
600 ml (20 fl oz) skimmed milk

25 g (1 oz) cocoa powder
25 g (1 oz) caster sugar
3 eggs, beaten
50 g (1¾ oz) plain chocolate chips

---

1. Preheat the oven to Gas Mark 4/180°C/fan oven 160°C. Spread each slice of bread lightly with the low fat spread and cut into quarters.

2. Arrange the bread, buttered side up, over the base of a shallow ovenproof dish.

3. Heat the milk until just boiling, and whisk in the cocoa powder and caster sugar. Pour in the beaten eggs and whisk well.

4. Sprinkle the chocolate chips over the bread slices and then strain the chocolate milk over the bread. Leave the dish to stand for 10 minutes, so the bread soaks up some of the liquid.

5. Bake the pudding for 35 minutes, until it is just firm to the touch. Allow it to stand for 5 minutes before serving.

Apple and blueberry crumble

15 Points per recipe | Takes 30 minutes to prepare, 25 minutes to bake

V *Serves 4. Calories per serving 235. Freeze* ✔

Serve this delicious crumble with a tablespoon of low fat fromage frais or custard, but don't forget to add the extra Points.

450 g (1 lb) cooking apples, peeled, cored and diced	For the crumble:
100 ml (3½ fl oz) fresh apple juice	**100 g (3½ oz) plain white flour**
1 tablespoon cornflour	**a pinch of ground cinnamon**
150 g (5½ oz) fresh or frozen blueberries	**25 g (1 oz) demerara sugar**
15 g (½ oz) granulated artificial sweetener	**50 g (1¾ oz) low fat spread, melted**

1. Preheat the oven to Gas Mark 4/180°C/fan oven 160°C.

2. Place the apples in a large saucepan with the apple juice and simmer gently for 5 minutes until they begin to soften.

3. Mix the cornflour with 2 tablespoons of cold water to make a thin paste. Add this to the apples and cook, stirring, until the liquid thickens.

4. Remove the pan from the heat and stir in the blueberries and artificial sweetener. Spoon the fruit into a 1.2 litre (2 pint) ovenproof dish.

5. Sift the flour and cinnamon into a mixing bowl and stir in the sugar. Drizzle over the melted low fat spread and mix well until you have a crumb mixture. Scatter the crumble mixture over the fruit and bake for 25 minutes, until the topping is crispy.

try this: *Why not use different combinations of filling such as pear and raspberry, or rhubarb and sliced banana? Remember to adjust the Points accordingly.*

Lemon sponges

11½ Points per recipe | Takes 20 minutes to prepare, 20 minutes to bake

V *Serves 4. Calories per serving 195. Freeze* ✔

The light, refreshing taste of lemon always goes down well. Try these luscious little sponges with a scoop of low Point vanilla ice cream and remember to add the extra Points.

low fat cooking spray	**50 g (1¾ oz) caster sugar**
4 teaspoons lemon curd	**100 g (3½ oz) plain white flour**
4 tablespoons boiling water	**finely grated zest of 1 lemon**
2 eggs	**1 tablespoon fresh lemon juice**

1. Preheat the oven to Gas Mark 4/180°C/fan oven 160°C. Spray four ramekin dishes with a little low fat cooking spray.

2. Mix the lemon curd with the boiling water. Divide this mixture equally between the ramekin dishes.

3. Using an electric beater, whisk together the eggs and caster sugar until they are pale and fluffy – when you lift the whisk the mixture should leave a trail.

4. Sift the flour into the egg mixture and, using a metal spoon, fold it in along with the lemon zest and lemon juice. Divide the mixture between the ramekin dishes and bake them in the oven for 20 minutes until the sponges are well risen and springy to the touch.

5. To serve, carefully run a round bladed knife around the edge of each dish and turn them out on to small serving plates.

tip: *Use heat resistant cups or china tea cups if you don't have individual ramekin dishes.*

Chocolate banana meringues

10½ Points per recipe | Takes 25 minutes to prepare, 1½ hours to bake + cooling

v *Serves 4. Calories per serving 200. Freeze ✗*

The crunchy texture of crisp meringue goes beautifully with creamy smooth yogurt.

---

2 egg whites

100 g (3½ oz) caster sugar

1 tablespoon cocoa powder

200 g pot of chocolate flavour low fat yogurt

(e.g. Müller Light)

2 bananas, peeled and sliced

---

1. Preheat the oven to Gas Mark 2/150°C/fan oven 130°C. Line two baking trays with non stick baking parchment.

2. Place the egg whites in a clean, large mixing bowl and whisk with electric beaters until they form soft peaks.

3. Gradually add the sugar, a spoonful at a time, whisking well until you have a smooth, thick, glossy meringue mixture. Sift in the cocoa powder and fold it in with a metal spoon.

4. Place four mounds of meringue mixture on the baking trays. Use a small spoon to form each mound into a basket shape, with a dip in the centre.

5. Bake for 1½ hours until the meringues are crisp. Allow them to cool.

6. When you are ready to serve, mix the yogurt and sliced bananas together. Spoon this into the centre of each meringue and serve.

tip: *Don't assemble this dish too early or the meringue will go soggy.*

Winter whip

8 Points per recipe | Takes 25 minutes + 2½–3½ hours chilling

v *Serves 4. Calories per serving 120. Freeze ✗*

This light and airy mousse is an ideal way to liven up winter fruits.

---

225 g (8 oz) blackberries

225 g (8 oz) plums, stoned and quartered

175 g (6 oz) pears, peeled, cored and diced

15 g (½ oz) granulated artificial sweetener

200 g (7 oz) low fat soft cheese

1 egg white

---

1. Place the blackberries, plums and pears in a large saucepan with the sweetener. Cover and heat gently for 5 minutes until the fruit is soft.

2. Push the cooked fruit through a sieve, discard the seeds and chill the purée in the fridge for 30 minutes.

3. Place the soft cheese in a mixing bowl and beat it with a wooden spoon to soften it. Gradually add the fruit purée and whisk well.

4. Whisk the egg white until it forms soft peaks and fold this into the fruit mixture. Divide the mixture between four individual glass dishes and chill for 2–3 hours.

tip: *For a firmer mousse, you can dissolve a teaspoon of gelatine in a little water and whisk this into the fruit before adding the soft cheese. The Points per serving will remain the same.*

Pineapple tarte tatin

19½ Points per recipe | **Takes 15 minutes to prepare, 25 minutes to bake + 10 minutes cooling**

V *Serves 8. Calories per serving 130. Freeze ✓*

1 teaspoon of plain white flour, for rolling	15 g (½ oz) polyunsaturated margarine, melted
150 g (5½ oz) puff pastry	
227 g can of pineapple rings in natural juice, drained and halved	2 tablespoons demerara sugar

1. Preheat the oven to Gas Mark 5/190°C/fan oven 170°C.
2. Lightly dust a work surface with flour and roll out the puff pastry to make a 23 cm (9 inch) circle.
3. Arrange the pineapple rings in a 20 cm (8 inch) heavy based frying pan with a metal handle, or a round cake tin. Drizzle the melted margarine over the pineapple and then sprinkle over the demerara sugar. Lay the pastry circle over the top of the fruit and tuck in the edges.
4. Bake the tart in the oven for 25 minutes. Allow it to cool for 10 minutes. Then place a plate on top and turn the pan or tin upside down so the tart drops on to the plate. Serve the tart warm or cold, sliced into wedges.

tip: *Make sure you use a good quality non stick pan or tin for this very simple yet effective dessert.*

try this: *Canned peach halves or apricots also make a good alternative to the pineapple in this recipe. The Points per serving will remain the same.*

Winter fruit compote with port

6 Points per recipe | **Takes 20 minutes + 2 hours cooling + 2 hours chilling**

V **Vg** *Serves 2. Calories per serving 215. Freeze ✗*

This fruit compote will keep in the fridge for up to a week in a sealed container as the port helps to preserve it.

225 g (8 oz) pears, peeled, cored and sliced	50 ml (2 fl oz) port
175 g (6 oz) plums, quartered and stoned	1 cinnamon stick
225 g (8 oz) apples, peeled, cored and sliced	2 cloves
	finely pared zest of 1 orange
50 g (1¾ oz) dried prunes, sliced	150 ml (5 fl oz) apple juice

1. Place all the ingredients in a large saucepan.
2. Bring the pan to the boil, reduce the heat, and simmer for 10 minutes over a low heat.
3. Remove the pan from the heat and allow the mixture to cool completely – this will take about 2 hours. Remove the cinnamon stick and cloves, and then chill in the fridge for at least 2 hours before serving.

Baked apple custards

6 Points per recipe | **Takes 20 minutes to prepare, 25 minutes to bake**

Ⓥ *Serves 4. Calories per serving 110. Freeze ✗*

These comforting little cups of apple flavoured egg custard are just the thing when you feel like a treat.

350 g (12 oz) cooking apples, peeled, cored and diced	300 ml (10 fl oz) skimmed milk
1 tablespoon clear honey	15 g (½ oz) granulated artificial sweetener
25 g (1 oz) custard powder	1 egg, separated
	a pinch of ground nutmeg

1. Preheat the oven to Gas Mark 2/150°C/fan oven 130°C.
2. Place the apples and honey in a small saucepan with 1 tablespoon of water. Cover and simmer gently for 5 minutes until the apples begin to soften.
3. Whisk the custard powder into the milk and heat gently in a small saucepan until you have a smooth, thick custard. Remove the pan from the heat and beat in the artificial sweetener, egg yolk and cooked apples.
4. Whisk the egg white until it forms soft peaks and fold it into the apple custard. Divide the mixture between four ramekin dishes. Sprinkle a little ground nutmeg over each one and bake for 25 minutes. Serve warm.

tip: *If you don't have ramekin dishes, use heat resistant china cups instead.*

Strawberry soufflé omelette

4 Points per recipe | **Takes 25 minutes**

Ⓥ *Serves 1. Calories per serving 270. Freeze ✗*

When you want something filling but fancy, and sweet rather than savoury, this fits the bill!

2 eggs, separated	1 tablespoon reduced sugar strawberry jam
2 tablespoons skimmed milk	low fat cooking spray
1 teaspoon caster sugar	
100 g (3½ oz) fresh strawberries, hulled and sliced	

1. Beat the egg yolks with the milk and caster sugar.
2. Whisk the egg whites until they form stiff peaks and fold them into the egg yolk mixture.
3. Mix the sliced strawberries with the strawberry jam and set aside.
4. Spray a 19 cm (7½ inch) non stick frying pan with low fat cooking spray and add the egg mixture. Cover and cook over a medium to low heat for 5 minutes, until the egg begins to set.
5. Scatter the strawberry mixture over the omelette and, using a wooden spatula, fold one side of the omelette over the other. Transfer it to a warmed plate and eat at once.

tip: *Make sure you use a clean, grease free bowl when you whisk the egg whites.*

Hot trifle

6 Points per recipe | **Takes 20 minutes to prepare, 10 minutes to bake**

(V) *Serves 4. Calories per serving 165. Freeze ✗*

Trifle is such a versatile dessert as you can use so many different combinations of fruit. This hot version is a wonderful low Point treat for a special meal.

4 sponge fingers	**150 ml pot of low fat custard**
275 g (9½ oz) frozen raspberries, defrosted	**2 egg whites**
100 ml (3½ fl oz) cranberry juice	**25 g (1 oz) caster sugar**
1 tablespoon artificial granulated sweetener	

1. Break each sponge finger into pieces and divide them between four heatproof individual dishes – glass ramekins are ideal as then you can see all the layers.
2. Mix together the raspberries, cranberry juice and sweetener and spoon this on top of the sponge pieces.
3. Preheat the oven to Gas Mark 5/190°C/fan oven 170°C. Spoon equal amounts of custard over each dish.
4. Whisk the egg whites until they form soft peaks. Fold in the sugar and then whisk again until you have a glossy meringue mixture.
5. Spoon the meringue mixture over each dish and use the back of a spoon to form rough peaks. Bake for 10 minutes until the meringue topping is pale golden. Serve at once.

try this: *Other fruits, such as sliced strawberries or blueberries, can be used instead of raspberries. Remember to adjust the Points accordingly.*

Boozy sticky toffee bananas

7 Points per recipe | **Takes 20 minutes**

(V) *Serves 2. Calories per serving 215. Freeze ✗*

This recipe is an excellent way of using up bananas when they've gone past their best.

15 g (½ oz) polyunsaturated margarine	**2 tablespoons dark rum**
a pinch of ground cinnamon	**2 bananas, peeled**
1 tablespoon golden syrup	

1. Melt the margarine in a small frying pan, and add the cinnamon, golden syrup and rum. Cook until the mixture bubbles.
2. Slice the bananas in half lengthways and then cut across each half. Add the banana pieces to the pan and cook for 5–8 minutes, spooning the pan juices over the bananas, until they begin to soften.
3. Serve the bananas with the pan juices spooned over them.

tip: *This is really delicious served with 1 tablespoon of half fat crème fraîche. This will add 1½ Points per serving.*

cakes...

and bakes

Marbled vanilla and coffee cake

34½ Points per recipe | **Takes 20 minutes to prepare, 35 minutes to bake**

(V) *Makes 12 slices. Calories per serving 170. Freeze* ✓

This is great fun to make. The best part is slicing into the cake and seeing the marbled patterns!

100 g (3½ oz) polyunsaturated margarine	**3 tablespoons strong black coffee**
100 g (3½ oz) caster sugar	For the topping:
2 eggs	**100 g (3½ oz) low fat soft cheese**
175 g (6 oz) self raising white flour	**1 teaspoon strong black coffee**
3 tablespoons skimmed milk	**2 tablespoons granulated artificial**
1 teaspoon vanilla essence	**sweetener**

1. Preheat the oven to Gas Mark 5/190°C/fan oven 170°C. Line a 20 cm (8 inch) round cake tin with non stick baking parchment.

2. Cream together the margarine and sugar until the mixture is pale and fluffy. Add the eggs and beat well. Sift the flour into the mixture and fold it in thoroughly using a metal spoon.

3. Divide the mixture between two bowls. Mix the skimmed milk and vanilla essence into one bowl, and the coffee into the other.

4. Drop alternating spoonfuls of the mixture into the prepared tin, dragging a skewer through the mixtures to blend them into each other. Bake for 30–35 minutes, until the cake is well risen and springy to the touch.

5. Carefully remove the cake from the tin and allow it to cool completely on a wire rack.

6. To decorate, beat the soft cheese with the coffee and sweetener and spread it over the surface, using a fork to mark a pattern on the top.

3½ POINTS

Summer fruit gâteau

28 Points per recipe | **Takes 25 minutes to prepare, 15 minutes to bake + 1 hour cooling**

V *Makes 8 slices. Calories per serving 230. Freeze ✓ (see tip)*

When there are lots of succulent summer fruits available, make the most of them with this mouth watering gâteau.

For the sponge:

3 eggs

175 g (6 oz) caster sugar

175 g (6 oz) plain white flour

finely grated zest of 1 orange

2 tablespoons orange juice

For the filling:

150 ml (5 fl oz) low fat strawberry fromage frais

125 g (4½ oz) fresh strawberries, hulled

100 g (3½ oz) fresh raspberries

1 nectarine, stoned and diced

50 g (1¾ oz) fresh blueberries

1 teaspoon icing sugar, to dust

1. Preheat the oven to Gas Mark 5/190°C/fan oven 170°C. Line the base of two 18 cm (7 inch) round cake tins with non stick baking parchment.

2. Using electric beaters, whisk the eggs and caster sugar together for at least 5 minutes until very pale and fluffy. Sift the flour into the mixture and fold it in carefully, using a metal spoon – don't stir it too much or you will knock the air out of the mixture.

3. Carefully fold in the orange zest and orange juice, and then divide the mixture between the two prepared tins. Bake for 12–15 minutes until the sponges are golden and springy to the touch. Transfer them to a wire rack and allow them to cool completely.

4. When cool, spread one of the cakes with the fromage frais, scatter over most of the prepared fruits, reserving a few for the top, and then place the other sponge cake on top. Dust the surface with sifted icing sugar and top with the reserved fruit.

tip: *You can freeze the sponges. Wrap them individually and freeze for up to two months. Allow them to defrost at room temperature and then assemble the gâteau with the filling ingredients.*

Family favourite

These delicious recipes are ideal for enjoying with the family at the weekend – they'll never know it's diet food.

Spicy spaghetti bolognese *page 61*, 1 serving.........5 Points

Summer fruit gâteau *above*, 1 serving...............3½ Points
(pictured left)

Total Points for meal.........................8½ Points

Christmas pudding

25½ Points per recipe | Takes 20 minutes to prepare, 2½ hours to bake + 1 hour standing

(v) Serves 8. Calories per serving 210. Freeze ✗

Just because you are watching your weight, it doesn't mean you have to miss out on Christmas pudding.

100 g (3½ oz) raisins	finely grated zest and juice of 1 orange
100 g (3½ oz) sultanas	75 g (2¾ oz) self raising white flour
100 g (3½ oz) currants	2 teaspoons mixed spice
150 ml (5 fl oz) hot, freshly made black tea	75 g (2¾ oz) fresh white breadcrumbs
50 g (1¾ oz) glacé cherries, chopped	50 g (1¾ oz) muscovado sugar
100 g (3½ oz) carrots, grated	1 egg, beaten
2 tablespoons rum or brandy	low fat cooking spray

1. Place the raisins, sultanas and currants in a large mixing bowl and pour over the hot tea. Leave to stand for 1 hour or until the fruit soaks up most of the tea.
2. Stir the glacé cherries, carrots, rum or brandy, and orange zest and juice into the soaked fruit.
3. Sift the flour into a large mixing bowl with the mixed spice, stir in the breadcrumbs, sugar and the fruit mixture. Add the beaten egg and mix thoroughly.
4. Lightly spray a 1.2 litre (2 pint) pudding basin with low fat cooking spray and spoon the pudding mixture into it. Level the surface with the back of a spoon and cover the basin with a double layer of pleated non stick baking parchment. Secure the parchment with string.
5. Pour some water into the base of a steamer or large saucepan with a tight fitting lid. Place the pudding in the steamer or pan, making sure that the water comes a quarter of the way up the sides of the basin. Steam for 2½ hours.
6. Carefully remove the pudding from the pan or steamer. Take off the baking parchment and run a round bladed knife around the edge of the basin. Turn out the pudding on to a serving plate.

tip: *For a dramatic entrance on Christmas day, you can flambé your pudding. To do this, gently heat 2 tablespoons of brandy in a metal ladle over a gas flame or electric ring. When the brandy is warm, drizzle it over the pudding and carefully set it alight – taking care not to burn your fingers! If you do this, the Points per serving will remain the same.*

Fruited tea loaf

25½ Points per recipe | Takes 10 minutes to prepare, 1 hour to bake + 30 minutes standing

(v) Serves 12. Calories per serving 145. Freeze ✓

100 g (3½ oz) All Bran	300 ml (10 fl oz) skimmed milk
125 g (4½ oz) caster sugar	125 g (4½ oz) courgettes, grated
1 teaspoon ground mixed spice	100 g (3½ oz) self raising white flour
225 g (8 oz) mixed dried fruit	

1. Preheat the oven to Gas Mark 4/180°C/fan oven 160°C. Line a 700 g (1 lb 9 oz) loaf tin with baking parchment.
2. Place the All Bran, sugar, mixed spice, and dried fruit into a mixing bowl and stir thoroughly. Stir in the milk and leave the mixture to stand for 30 minutes.
3. Stir in the courgettes and sift in the flour. Mix well and then spoon the mixture into the loaf tin, and level the surface with the back of a spoon. Bake for 1 hour or until a skewer inserted into the centre comes out clean.
4. Transfer the loaf to a cooling rack and allow it to cool before cutting it into slices.

tip: *As there is no fat in this tea bread it will only last for up to three days, so wrap it well and store it in a cool place.*

Nutmeg and yogurt scone squares

18½ Points per recipe | Takes 15 minutes to prepare, 15 minutes to bake

V *Makes 9 scones. Calories per serving 125. Freeze ✓*

When friends or family arrive unexpectedly, surprise them with these super speedy scones that can be prepared and cooked all within half an hour.

225 g (8 oz) self raising white flour, plus 1 tablespoon for rolling	25 g (1 oz) polyunsaturated margarine
½ teaspoon ground nutmeg	25 g (1 oz) caster sugar
¼ teaspoon salt	150 ml (5 fl oz) low fat plain yogurt
	1 tablespoon skimmed milk

1. Preheat the oven to Gas Mark 6/200°C/fan oven 180°C. Line a baking tray with non stick baking parchment.
2. Sift the flour into a mixing bowl with the nutmeg and salt. Rub in the margarine, using your fingertips, until the mixture resembles fine breadcrumbs. Stir in the sugar and then make a well in the centre. Place the yogurt in the well and then mix it all to form a soft dough.
3. Sprinkle a clean work surface with the extra flour. Roll out the dough to a 23 cm (9 inch) square. Cut the square into nine smaller squares. Place each square on the lined baking tray and brush the tops with skimmed milk.
4. Bake for 12–15 minutes until well risen and golden.

tip: *These are delicious split and served with a heaped teaspoon of reduced sugar jam, the Points per serving will then be 2½.*

Easy rosemary beer bread

20½ Points per recipe | Takes 15 minutes to prepare, 30 minutes to bake

V *Vg* *Makes 10 slices. Calories per serving 120. Freeze ✓*

This clever recipe uses real ale to bind everything together, which gives the bread a wonderful yeasty flavour.

350 g (12 oz) wholemeal flour	2 teaspoons finely chopped fresh rosemary
1 teaspoon baking powder	½ teaspoon salt
25 g (1 oz) sun dried tomatoes, chopped finely	300 ml (10 fl oz) real ale
	2 teaspoons olive oil

1. Preheat the oven to Gas Mark 6/200°C/fan oven 180°C. Line a 700 g (1 lb 9 oz) loaf tin with non stick baking parchment.
2. Place the wholemeal flour in a bowl and stir in the baking powder, chopped sun dried tomatoes, rosemary and salt.
3. Make a well in the centre of the dry ingredients. Add the ale and olive oil, and mix to a firm dough. Press the dough into the loaf tin and score the top. Bake for 30 minutes, until well risen and the base of the bread sounds hollow when tapped.

tip: *If you can, use good quality extra virgin olive oil; it can be expensive but makes all the difference.*

try this: *Try other flavours instead of the tomatoes, such as a teaspoon of wholegrain mustard or 25 g (1 oz) sliced, stoned black olives, but remember to alter the Points accordingly.*

Hot cross buns

33½ Points per recipe | Takes 25 minutes to prepare, 20 minutes to bake + 1½ hours rising

(V) *Makes 16 buns. Calories per serving 135. Freeze ✓*

350 g (12 oz) strong white flour, plus
   2 tablespoons for kneading

100 g (3½ oz) granary flour

15 g (½ oz) easy blend yeast

1 teaspoon caster sugar

½ teaspoon salt

1 teaspoon ground mixed spice

50 g (1¾ oz) currants

50 g (1¾ oz) chopped mixed peel

150 ml (5 fl oz) hand hot water

150 ml (5 fl oz) hand hot skimmed milk

25 g (1 oz) polyunsaturated margarine,
   melted

low fat cooking spray

1 tablespoon clear honey, warmed

1. Sift the strong white flour into a mixing bowl. Stir in the granary flour, easy blend yeast, sugar, salt, mixed spice, currants and mixed peel.

2. Mix together the water, milk and melted margarine and pour this over the dry ingredients. Using clean hands, mix thoroughly until you have a soft dough.

3. Turn out the dough on to a clean work surface and, using a little of the extra flour to prevent sticking, knead the dough for 5 minutes.

4. Lightly spray a large bowl with low fat cooking spray – this will prevent the dough from sticking. Place the dough in the bowl and cover with a damp tea towel. Leave the dough to rise in a warm place for 1 hour.

5. Turn the dough out on to a lightly floured surface and knead again for 2–3 minutes. Divide the dough into 16 pieces and shape them into balls.

6. Arrange the dough balls on two non stick baking trays and, using a sharp knife, mark a cross on the top of each one. Cover both trays with a damp tea towel again and leave in a warm place for 30 minutes, until the buns have risen. Preheat the oven to Gas Mark 6/200°C/fan oven 180°C.

7. Bake the buns for 15–20 minutes, until they are golden. To test if they are cooked, tap the base of the buns – they should sound hollow.

8. Transfer the buns to a cooling rack and brush the tops with a little warmed honey while they are still hot.

Raisin and honey flapjacks

41½ Points per recipe | Takes 15 minutes to prepare, 20 minutes to bake

(V) *Makes 10 flapjacks. Calories per serving 250. Freeze ✗*

125 g (4½ oz) polyunsaturated margarine

125 g (4½ oz) demerara sugar

3 tablespoons clear honey

50 g (1¾ oz) raisins

1 teaspoon ground mixed spice

200 g (7 oz) rolled oats

1. Preheat the oven to Gas Mark 5/190°C/fan oven 170°C. Line a 20 cm (8 inch) non stick square baking tin with non stick baking parchment.

2. Place the margarine, sugar and honey in a small saucepan and heat gently until dissolved.

3. Mix in the raisins, mixed spice and rolled oats. Press the mixture into the prepared tin and level with the back of a metal spoon. Bake for 20 minutes.

4. Mark out 10 fingers while the flapjack is still warm.

tip: *Flapjacks should have a soft, chewy texture so take care not to overcook them, or they will become brittle.*

Simple scones

23½ Points per recipe | Takes 15 minutes to prepare, 15 minutes to bake

V *Makes 10 scones. Calories per serving 145. Freeze ✓*

These melt in the mouth scones are the perfect afternoon treat!

---

225 g (8 oz) self raising white flour, plus	**25 g (1 oz) caster sugar**
2 teaspoons for rolling	**50 g (1¾ oz) sultanas**
½ teaspoon baking powder	**150 ml (5 fl oz) skimmed milk, plus**
½ teaspoon salt	**2 tablespoons for glazing**
50 g (1¾ oz) polyunsaturated margarine	**1 egg white**

---

1. Preheat the oven to Gas Mark 6/200°C/fan oven180°C.

2. Sift the flour and baking powder into a mixing bowl and add the salt. Rub in the margarine, using your fingertips, until the mixture resembles fine breadcrumbs. Stir in the caster sugar and sultanas.

3. Make a well in the centre of the flour mixture and pour in the milk. Whisk the egg white until it forms soft peaks, and add it to the well. Fold all the wet ingredients into the dry ingredients and mix to form a soft dough.

4. Roll out the dough on a lightly floured board and cut out ten 5 cm (2 inch) circles. Place the scones on a non stick baking tray and brush the tops with milk. Bake for 12–15 minutes, until they are well risen and golden.

tip: *Scones really are best eaten warm, so try giving them a 10 second blast in the microwave on High just before serving.*

Banana and poppyseed tea bread

37 Points per recipe | Takes 25 minutes to prepare, 1 hour to bake

V *Makes 8 slices. Calories per serving 290. Freeze ✓*

Fructose is a fruit sugar that is sweeter than sucrose – the sugar we generally use in cooking. Because fructose is sweeter we need to use less of it. It is generally available in all major supermarkets.

---

2 small bananas	**1 tablespoon poppy seeds**
2 tablespoons fresh lemon juice	**2 eggs, beaten**
100 g (3½ oz) polyunsaturated margarine	**225 g (8 oz) self raising white flour**
100 g (3½ oz) fructose	**1 teaspoon baking powder**
½ teaspoon grated nutmeg	

---

1. Preheat the oven to Gas Mark 3/160°C/fan oven 140°C. Line a 700 g (1 lb 9 oz) loaf tin with non stick baking parchment.

2. Peel the bananas and mash them thoroughly with the lemon juice, and set aside.

3. Cream together the margarine and fructose until you have a pale and fluffy mixture. Add the nutmeg, poppy seeds, mashed bananas and beaten eggs.

4. Sift the flour and baking powder into the mixture and fold it in thoroughly. Spoon it all into the prepared tin and level the top with the back of a metal spoon. Bake for 1 hour, or until a skewer inserted into the centre comes out clean.

tip: *Store in an airtight container for up to one week.*

Banana and nutmeg squares

36½ Points per recipe | Takes 25 minutes to prepare, 40 minutes to bake

Makes 16 squares. Calories per serving 145. Freeze ✓ (undecorated)

This is a great way to use up any over ripe bananas. The topping adds a delicious crunch.

---

75 g (2¾ oz) polyunsaturated margarine

100 g (3½ oz) demerara sugar

2 eggs

2 bananas, mashed

2 tablespoons reduced sugar marmalade

1 teaspoon ground nutmeg

175 g (6 oz) self raising white flour

For the topping:

150 g (5½ oz) low fat soft cheese

25 g (1 oz) banana chips, crumbled

grated zest of 1 orange

---

1. Preheat the oven to Gas Mark 4/180°C/fan oven 160°C. Line a non stick 20 cm (8 inch) loose bottomed square cake tin with non stick baking parchment.

2. Cream together the margarine and sugar, and then add the eggs, one at a time, and beat well. Mix in the mashed bananas, marmalade and nutmeg.

3. Sift the flour into the bowl and fold it thoroughly into the banana mixture. Spoon the cake mixture into the prepared tin, levelling it with the back of a spoon. Bake for 40 minutes, until well risen and springy to the touch.

4. Carefully transfer the cake to a cooling rack and allow it to cool completely. When cool, gently beat the soft cheese a little to soften it. Spread it over the top of the cake and sprinkle the surface with banana chips and orange zest. Cut it into 16 squares.

tip: *To save on Points you can leave the topping off, this will make each square 2 Points.*

goes well with...

a steaming hot cup of tea!

Chocolate victoria sponge

17½ Points per recipe | **Takes 25 minutes to prepare, 20 minutes to bake**

Makes 8 slices. Calories per serving 145. Freeze ✓ (sponges only)

There is something very appealing about a chocolate cake, and this fat free sponge isn't as naughty as it looks!

3 eggs

75 g (2¾ oz) caster sugar

75 g (2¾ oz) plain white flour

25 g (1 oz) cocoa powder

For the filling:

3 tablespoons reduced sugar strawberry jam

100 ml (3½ fl oz) 0% fat Greek style plain
   yogurt

To decorate:

1 teaspoon icing sugar

15 g (½ oz) plain chocolate curls

1. Preheat the oven to Gas Mark 4/180°C/fan oven 160°C. Line the base of two 19 cm (7½ inch) round non stick cake tins with non stick baking parchment.

2. Place the eggs and caster sugar in a mixing bowl and whisk with electric beaters for 5 minutes, until you have a pale, fluffy mixture – when you lift the whisk, it should leave a trail.

3. Sift in the flour and cocoa powder and fold them in using a metal spoon, taking care not to knock too much air out. Divide the mixture between the two tins and bake for 20 minutes, until the sponges are firm and springy to the touch. Transfer the cakes to a wire rack to cool completely.

4. When cool, spread one of the cakes with the jam, top with the yogurt and place the second cake over the top. Put the cake on a serving plate and dust the top with icing sugar, and then scatter the chocolate curls over the top.

try this: *Real chocolate lovers can use low fat chocolate yogurt for the filling instead of Greek yogurt. The Points per serving will remain the same.*

Cranberry spiced muffins

32 Points per recipe | **Takes 15 minutes to prepare, 20 minutes to bake**

Ⓥ *Makes 12 muffins. Calories per serving 180. Freeze ✓*

These days, cranberries are easily available all year round. They add a wonderful tang to these delicious muffins.

300 g (10½ oz) plain white flour

2 teaspoons baking powder

½ teaspoon ground cinnamon

½ teaspoon ground nutmeg

finely grated zest of 1 orange

125 g (4½ oz) demerara sugar

75 g (2¾ oz) frozen cranberries, defrosted

50 ml (2 fl oz) sunflower oil

225 ml (8 fl oz) skimmed milk

1 egg

1. Preheat the oven to Gas Mark 6/200°C/fan oven 180°C. Line a 12 hole muffin tray with paper cases.

2. Sift the flour and baking powder into a mixing bowl and stir in the cinnamon, nutmeg and orange zest. Add the sugar and cranberries.

3. Beat together the oil, milk and egg and pour this over the dry ingredients. Mix well with a wooden spoon to make a soft batter. Spoon the mixture in the paper cases and bake for 15–20 minutes, until the muffins are well risen and golden.

try this: *Cranberries are quite a sharp fruit – if you prefer something sweeter use sultanas or raisins instead. The Points will then be 3 per muffin.*

Cheese scone wedges

25 Points per recipe | Takes 15 minutes to prepare, 15 minutes to bake

(V) *Makes 8 wedges. Calories per serving 185. Freeze* ✓

Sometimes we crave a savoury rather than a sweet snack — these fit the bill perfectly.

---

225 g (8 oz) self raising white flour

1 teaspoon baking powder

a pinch of salt

½ teaspoon English mustard powder

50 g (1¾ oz) polyunsaturated margarine

75 g (2¾ oz) half fat Red Leicester cheese, grated

1 egg, beaten

150 ml (5 fl oz) skimmed milk

---

1. Preheat the oven to Gas Mark 7/220°C/fan oven 200°C.

2. Sift the flour and baking powder into a mixing bowl with the salt and mustard powder. Rub in the margarine, using your fingertips, until the mixture resembles fine breadcrumbs. Stir in the cheese and make a well in the centre.

3. Beat together the egg and milk and pour this into the well. Mix together the dry and wet ingredients to form a soft dough. Shape the dough into a 20 cm (8 inch) circle and place it on a non stick baking tray.

4. Mark eight wedges on the surface of the dough. Bake the scone for 15 minutes, until it is well risen and golden.

tip: *Try not to over handle the dough, it doesn't require kneading as this will make the scones tough.*

Potato and chive cakes

8½ Points per recipe | Takes 45 minutes

(V) *Makes 8 cakes. Calories per serving 75. Freeze* ✓

When you feel like something a little bit more exciting than bread, try one of these tasty little potato cakes. They're at their best served warm.

---

225 g (8 oz) potatoes, peeled and diced

100 g (3½ oz) plain white flour

½ teaspoon salt

2 tablespoons finely chopped fresh chives

1 egg, separated

low fat cooking spray

salt and freshly ground black pepper

---

1. Cook the potatoes in lightly salted, boiling water, until tender. Drain and mash them thoroughly. Allow to cool for 10 minutes and then beat in the flour, salt, chives, black pepper and egg yolk.

2. Whisk the egg white until it forms soft peaks and fold it into the potato mixture. Divide the mixture into eight and shape into rough circles.

3. Spray a heavy based, non stick frying pan with low fat cooking spray and heat gently. Cook the potato cakes over a medium to low heat for 5 minutes on each side, until they are golden and cooked through.

tip: *These make an excellent breakfast treat, serve them with grilled mushrooms or grilled tomatoes, or even top with a poached egg — don't forget to add the extra Points.*

Corn bread

37½ Points per recipe | Takes 15 minutes to prepare, 25 minutes to bake

V *Makes 12 squares. Calories per serving 205. Freeze* ✓

This is the perfect accompaniment to a pot of chilli. Try it with the Chilli Con Carne on page 142.

225 g (8 oz) cornmeal	**2 eggs**
225 g (8 oz) self raising white flour	**300 ml (10 fl oz) low fat plain yogurt**
1 teaspoon baking powder	**4 tablespoons skimmed milk**
1 teaspoon salt	**50 ml (2 fl oz) vegetable oil**
100 g (3½ oz) canned sweetcorn, drained	

1. Preheat the oven to Gas Mark 5/190°C/fan oven 170°C. Line a 20 cm (8 inch) square non stick baking tin with non stick baking parchment.

2. Place the cornmeal in a bowl and sift in the flour and baking powder. Stir in the salt and sweetcorn.

3. Beat the eggs with the yogurt, milk and vegetable oil and add this mixture to the dry ingredients. Mix well to a soft dropping consistency and then spoon it into the prepared tin. Bake for 25 minutes until well risen.

4. Transfer to a wire rack and cool before cutting into 12 squares.

tip: *Cornmeal is a yellow grain which, when cooked, gives a wonderful golden colour to your bread. It is available in most large supermarkets and health food stores.*

Italian buns

26 Points per recipe | Takes 25 minutes to prepare, 20 minutes to bake + 1½ hours rising

V **Vg** *Makes 8 buns. Calories per serving 215. Freeze* ✓

Try serving one of these Mediterranean style buns with a warming soup for a hearty lunchtime filler.

450 g (1 lb) strong white flour, plus	**15 g (½ oz) fresh basil, torn**
1 tablespoon extra for kneading	**25 g (1 oz) stoned green or black olives, diced**
1 teaspoon salt	**300 ml (10 fl oz) hand hot water**
1 sachet easy blend yeast	**1 tablespoon extra virgin olive oil**
1 teaspoon caster sugar	**freshly ground mixed pepper**

1. Sift the flour into a warmed mixing bowl. Stir in the salt, yeast, sugar, basil and olives.

2. Add the water and, using clean hands, bring the mixture together to form a dough ball. Knead the dough on a lightly floured surface for 5 minutes.

3. Place the dough in a clean bowl, cover with a damp tea towel and leave it to rise for 1 hour.

4. Turn the dough out on to a clean surface and knead again for 2 minutes. Shape the dough into eight balls. Arrange them on a non stick baking tray, and cover them with a damp tea towel. Leave to rise in a warm place for about 30 minutes.

5. Preheat the oven to Gas Mark 6/200°C/fan oven 180°C. Brush the tops of the buns with olive oil and sprinkle the surface with a little freshly ground mixed pepper.

6. Bake the buns for 15–20 minutes until the bases sound hollow when tapped.

tip: *The secret of cooking with yeast is to keep everything warm, this allows the yeast to react and rise well. An airing cupboard is a good place to allow the dough to rise. Cold temperatures can slow down the process considerably.*

Chocolate and raspberry swiss roll

18 Points per recipe | Takes 20 minutes to prepare, 15 minutes to bake + 1 hour cooling

v *Serves 8 slices. Calories per serving 130. Freeze ✗*

Chocolate and raspberries are an unbeatable combination. This looks very impressive and yet it is so easy to make!

For the Swiss roll:

3 eggs

75 g (2¾ oz) caster sugar, plus 1 teaspoon extra for sprinkling

75 g (2¾ oz) plain white flour

25 g (1 oz) cocoa powder

2 tablespoons boiling water

2 drops vanilla essence

For the filling:

150 g pot of low fat raspberry fromage frais

100 g (3½ oz) fresh raspberries

1 teaspoon icing sugar

1. Preheat the oven to Gas Mark 6/200°C/fan oven 180°C. Line a 23 cm x 28 cm (9 inch × 11 inch) Swiss roll tin with non stick baking parchment.

2. Using electric beaters, whisk together the eggs and caster sugar, until the mixture is pale and foamy. Sift the flour and cocoa powder into the bowl, and, using a metal spoon, carefully fold this in with the water and vanilla essence.

3. Pour the mixture into the prepared tin, shaking the tin gently to level the surface. Bake for 12–15 minutes until the sponge is just springy to the touch.

4. Sprinkle a sheet of non stick baking parchment with the extra caster sugar and then turn out the sponge on to it. Peel away the lining paper and using the clean sheet as a guide, roll up the sponge – enclosing the paper. Allow the Swiss roll to cool for 1 hour.

5. Carefully unroll the sponge, spread it with the raspberry fromage frais and scatter over two thirds of the raspberries. Roll it up again and lay it on a serving platter.

6. Dust with the icing sugar and decorate it with the remaining raspberries.

tip: *It is important to work quickly when you remove the sponge from the oven and roll it up; if you allow it to cool too much, it will become brittle and won't roll easily. If you have difficulty when rolling, cover the sponge with a sheet of greaseproof paper and a damp tea towel, leave for 5 minutes and then try again.*

Cherry and sesame seed flapjacks

44 Points per recipe | Takes 15 minutes to prepare, 20 minutes to bake

v *Makes 10 flapjacks. Calories per serving 265. Freeze ✗*

Sesame seeds have an intense nutty flavour which combine wonderfully with the flavour of cherries in these chewy flapjacks.

125 g (4½ oz) polyunsaturated margarine

125 g (4½ oz) demerara sugar

3 tablespoons golden syrup

1 teaspoon ground cinnamon

50 g (1¾ oz) glacé cherries, chopped roughly

200 g (7 oz) rolled oats

2 tablespoons sesame seeds

1. Preheat the oven to Gas Mark 5/190°C/fan oven 170°C. Line a 20 cm (8 inch) non stick square baking tin with non stick baking parchment.

2. Place the margarine, sugar and syrup in a small saucepan and heat gently until they are dissolved.

3. Stir in the cinnamon, cherries, rolled oats and sesame seeds, and mix thoroughly. Press the mixture into the prepared tin and bake for 20 minutes.

4. Mark out 10 fingers while the flapjack is still warm.

Oaty crumbles

24 Points per recipe | **Takes 20 minutes to prepare, 15 minutes to bake**

V *Makes 16 biscuits. Calories per serving 90. Freeze ✓*

These crunchy little biscuits are so easy to make. Make a batch to keep handy when you feel like something to nibble.

75 g (2¾ oz) plain white flour	½ teaspoon ground nutmeg
75 g (2¾ oz) demerara sugar	75 g (2¾ oz) polyunsaturated margarine
75 g (2¾ oz) porridge oats	1 tablespoon clear honey

1. Preheat the oven to Gas Mark 4/180°C/fan oven 160°C. Line two baking trays with non stick baking parchment.

2. Mix together the flour, sugar, oats, and nutmeg.

3. Melt the margarine in a small saucepan with the honey and then pour it over the dry ingredients. Mix well and place 16 spoonfuls of the mixture, set well apart, on to the prepared baking trays.

4. Bake for 15 minutes until the biscuits have spread out and are golden brown. Allow them to cool on the baking trays for 5 minutes and then transfer them to a wire rack to cool completely.

tip: *You can store these biscuits in an airtight container for up to one week.*

Yorkshire curd tarts

24 Points per recipe | **Takes 20 minutes to prepare, 20 minutes to bake**

V *Makes 12 tarts. Calories per serving 115. Freeze ✓*

These melt in the mouth treats are rather like mini cheesecakes, but are much lower in Points!

175 g (6 oz) ready made shortcrust pastry, defrosted if frozen	25 g (1 oz) sultanas
125 g (4½ oz) low fat cottage cheese	25 g (1 oz) demerara sugar
finely grated zest of 1 lemon	a pinch of ground nutmeg
	1 egg

1. Preheat the oven to Gas Mark 5/190°C/fan oven 170°C. Roll out the pastry and cut out circles. Fit them in a 12 hole patty tin.

2. Push the cottage cheese through a sieve and beat it well with the lemon zest, sultanas, sugar, nutmeg and egg.

3. Divide the filling between the pastry cases and bake for 20 minutes, until the filling is just set to the touch.

try this: *As a change, try adding grated orange zest instead of lemon and using ground cinnamon instead of the nutmeg. Dust 1 teaspoon of icing sugar over the total number of tarts, if desired, which will not alter the Points.*

Chocolate and banana slab cake

35 Points per recipe | Takes 20 minutes to prepare, 25 minutes to bake

V *Makes 12 slices. Calories per serving 175. Freeze ✗*

This rich and satisfying cake is absolutely heavenly – and each slice is only 3 Points.

175 g (6 oz) self raising white flour	2 small bananas, peeled and mashed
50 g (1¾ oz) cocoa powder	1 teaspoon vanilla essence
100 g (3½ oz) demerara sugar	1 tablespoon fresh lemon juice
100 g (3½ oz) polyunsaturated margarine, melted	

1. Preheat the oven to Gas Mark 4/180°C/fan oven 160°C. Line a 20 cm (8 inch) square tin with non stick baking parchment.

2. Sift the flour and cocoa powder into a mixing bowl and stir in the sugar.

3. Mix the margarine with the mashed bananas, vanilla essence and lemon juice and 200 ml (7 fl oz) cold water. Pour this mixture over the dry ingredients and mix well.

4. Pour the cake mixture into the prepared tin and bake for 25 minutes. Allow to cool in the tin for 15 minutes and then carefully transfer the cake to a wire rack to cool completely. Cut into 12 slices.

try this: *Add 50 g (1¾ oz) chopped pecan nuts to give an additional crunchy texture, adding ½ a Point per slice.*

Sticky carrot and ginger slices

38½ Points per recipe | Takes 25 minutes to prepare, 50 minutes to bake

V *Makes 12 slices. Calories per serving 205. Freeze ✓*

The carrots and treacle in this recipe make these slices fantastically moist.

350 g (12 oz) self raising white flour	150 g (5½ oz) carrots, grated
a pinch of salt	3 tablespoons treacle
1 tablespoon ground ginger	150 ml (5 fl oz) skimmed milk
75 g (2¾ oz) polyunsaturated margarine	2 eggs, beaten
75 g (2¾ oz) dark soft brown sugar	

1. Preheat the oven to Gas Mark 3/160°C/fan oven 140°C. Line an 18 cm × 28 cm (7 inch × 11 inch) rectangular cake tin with non stick baking parchment.

2. Sift the flour into a mixing bowl with the salt and ground ginger. Rub in the margarine, using your fingertips, until the mixture resembles fine breadcrumbs. Stir in the sugar and carrots.

3. Place the treacle in a small saucepan with the milk and warm gently, until the treacle has melted into the milk. Add this to the dry ingredients along with the beaten eggs and mix well.

4. Spoon the mixture into the prepared tin and bake for 50 minutes, until firm and springy to the touch. Turn out the cake on to a wire rack to cool, and then cut it into 12 slices.

Apple and cinnamon ring

25 Points per recipe | Takes 20 minutes to prepare, 40 minutes to bake

(V) *Makes 10 slices. Calories per serving 170. Freeze* ✓

low fat cooking spray	50 g (1¾ oz) demerara sugar
350 g (12 oz) cooking apples, peeled, cored and grated coarsely	50 g (1¾ oz) sultanas
	50 ml (2 fl oz) sunflower oil
2 tablespoons fresh lemon juice	2 eggs
150 g (5½ oz) self raising white flour	100 ml (3½ fl oz) skimmed milk
1 teaspoon baking powder	2 tablespoons reduced sugar apricot jam
½ teaspoon ground cinnamon	

1. Preheat the oven to Gas Mark 4/180°C/fan oven 160°C. Spray an 850 ml (1½ pint) ring mould with a little low fat cooking spray. Mix the grated apple with the lemon juice.

2. Sift the flour, baking powder and cinnamon into a mixing bowl. Stir in the grated apple mixture, sugar and sultanas. Make a well in the centre of the mixture.

3. Beat together the oil, eggs, milk and jam. Pour this into the well in the dry ingredients and mix everything together.

4. Spoon the mixture into the prepared mould and level the surface with the back of a spoon. Bake for 35–40 minutes, or until the cake is browned, firm and springy to the touch. Cool in the tin for 10 minutes then loosen the edges with a palette knife, and turn it out on to a cooling rack.

tip: *Before serving, dust with ½ a teaspoon of icing sugar, if desired. This will not alter the Points.*

Spicy fruit cake

41½ Points per recipe | Takes 20 minutes to prepare, 1¼ hours to bake

(V) *Makes 20 slices. Calories per serving 135. Freeze* ✓

Perfect for an Easter treat, or for those of you who don't like a heavy, rich, dark fruit cake at Christmas.

100 g (3½ oz) polyunsaturated margarine	50 g (1¾ oz) sultanas
100 g (3½ oz) light soft brown sugar	finely grated zest of 1 lemon
3 eggs, beaten	225 g (8 oz) self raising white flour
175 g (6 oz) carrots, grated	1 teaspoon baking powder
100 g (3½ oz) ready to eat dried apricots, chopped	½ teaspoon salt
	1 teaspoon ground mixed spice
50 g (1¾ oz) glacé cherries, chopped	1 teaspoon ground ginger

1. Preheat the oven to Gas Mark 4/180°C/fan oven 160°C. Line a 20 cm (8 inch) loose bottomed round cake tin with non stick baking parchment.

2. Cream together the margarine and sugar until fluffy, add the eggs and beat well. Stir in the grated carrots, apricots, glacé cherries, sultanas and lemon zest.

3. Sift in the flour, baking powder, salt, mixed spice and ginger and fold them in. Spoon the mixture into the tin and bake for 1¼ hours, until firm to the touch and a skewer inserted into the centre, comes out clean.

4. Carefully turn the cake out on to a wire rack and allow to cool completely before cutting into thin slices to serve.

tip: *You can keep this cake for up to a week, well wrapped in an airtight container and stored in a cool place.*

Luscious lemon fairy cakes

16 Points per recipe | Takes 10 minutes to prepare, 15 minutes to bake

v *Makes 9 cakes. Calories per serving 105. Freeze* ✓

The fresh, zesty flavour of lemons make these little cakes a popular treat.

---

75 g (2¾ oz) self raising white flour

50 g (1¾ oz) polyunsaturated margarine

50 g (1¾ oz) caster sugar

1 egg, beaten

finely grated zest of 1 lemon

1 tablespoon fresh lemon juice

For the topping:

1 tablespoon lemon curd

1 tablespoon boiling water

---

1. Preheat the oven to Gas Mark 5/190°C/fan oven 170°C. Line a 9 hole bun tin with paper cases.

2. Sift the flour into a bowl. In a separate mixing bowl beat the margarine and caster sugar together, until you have a pale and fluffy mixture. Add the beaten egg, lemon zest and lemon juice with 1 tablespoon of the flour and mix well.

3. Add the remaining flour to the lemon mixture and fold it in thoroughly. Divide the mixture between the paper cases and bake for 15 minutes, until the sponges are springy to the touch.

4. While the cakes are still warm, mix the lemon curd with the boiling water and brush this over the surface of the cakes. Allow them to cool before serving.

goes well with...

a coffee for a mid morning boost.

Marmalade muffins

23 Points per recipe | Takes 20 minutes to prepare, 20 minutes to bake

V *Makes 12 muffins. Calories per serving 125. Freeze ✓*

These mouth watering muffins are a firm family favourite.

225 g (8 oz) plain white flour	4 tablespoons reduced sugar marmalade
2 teaspoons baking powder	1 egg
a pinch of salt	100 ml (3½ fl oz) fresh orange juice
50 ml (2 fl oz) sunflower oil	100 ml (3½ fl oz) low fat plain yogurt

1. Preheat the oven to Gas Mark 6/200°C/fan oven 180°C. Line a 12 hole muffin tray with paper cases.
2. Sift the flour into a mixing bowl with the baking powder and salt.
3. Beat together the sunflower oil, marmalade, egg, orange juice and yogurt. Pour this mixture over the dry ingredients and stir to form a smooth, thick batter.
4. Divide the mixture between the paper cases and bake for 20 minutes, until the muffins are well risen and springy to the touch. Allow to cool on a wire rack and store in an airtight container for up to four days.

try this: *You can use a different flavoured reduced sugar jam such as blackcurrant, and substitute apple juice for the orange juice.*

Vanilla melting moments

25 Points per recipe | Takes 20 minutes to prepare, 15 minutes to bake

V *Makes 16 biscuits. Calories per serving 90. Freeze ✓*

Vanilla pods are more expensive than essence, but the difference in flavour is well worth it.

100 g (3½ oz) polyunsaturated margarine	75 g (2¾ oz) self raising white flour
50 g (1¾ oz) icing sugar	75 g (2¾ oz) cornflour
½ vanilla pod	

1. Preheat the oven to Gas Mark 4/180°C/fan oven 160°C. Line two baking trays with non stick baking parchment.
2. Place the margarine in a warmed mixing bowl and sift in the icing sugar. Cream them together until you have a pale and fluffy mixture.
3. Using a small, sharp knife, slice the vanilla pod in half lengthways. Scoop out the tiny black seeds and beat them into the creamed mixture. Add the flour and cornflour, and mix to form a stiff dough.
4. Divide the dough into 16 small balls. Arrange them well apart on the baking sheets and press them down with a fork.
5. Bake for 12–15 minutes until just golden. Cool on the baking trays for 10 minutes, and then, using a spatula, transfer them to a wire rack to allow them to cool and become crisp.

try this: *If you prefer, use ground mixed spice or cinnamon to flavour the melting moments instead of vanilla. The Points will remain the same.*

Italian lemon cake

20½ Points per recipe | Takes 30 minutes to prepare, 1 hour to bake + 30 minutes cooling

Ⓥ *Makes 10 slices. Calories per serving 130. Freeze* ✗

This is a very moist textured cake, almost like a pudding; the saffron gives it a wonderful, rich, golden yellow colour.

100 g (3½ oz) Arborio rice	50 g (1¾ oz) polyunsaturated margarine,
finely grated zest and juice of 1 lemon	melted
6 saffron strands	50 g (1¾ oz) polenta
425 ml (15 fl oz) boiling water	To decorate:
2 eggs	grated lemon zest
50 g (1¾ oz) fructose	1 teaspoon icing sugar

1. Place the rice in a large saucepan with the lemon zest and juice, saffron and the boiling water. Cover and simmer gently for 20 minutes, stirring from time to time, until the liquid has been absorbed and the rice is tender. Remove the pan from the heat and allow to cool for 30 minutes.

2. Preheat the oven to Gas Mark 3/160°C/fan oven 140°C. Line a 20 cm (8 inch) loose bottomed round cake tin with non stick baking parchment.

3. Using electric beaters, whisk together the eggs and fructose until pale and fluffy. While still whisking, add the melted margarine and then fold in the cooled rice mixture and polenta.

4. Spoon into the prepared tin and bake for 1 hour. Allow the cake to cool in the tin for 1 hour, and then carefully transfer it to a wire rack to cool completely. Decorate the top with grated lemon zest and icing sugar.

tip: *Although saffron is rather expensive, its flavour is so intense that you need only a little.*

Chocolate cherry brownies

39 Points per recipe | Takes 20 minutes to prepare, 25 minutes to bake

Ⓥ *Makes 12 brownies. Calories per serving 225. Freeze* ✓

175 g (6 oz) self raising white flour	175 ml (6 fl oz) skimmed milk
50 g (1¾ oz) cocoa powder	1 teaspoon almond essence
100 g (3½ oz) soft dark brown sugar	150 g (5½ oz) canned cherries, drained
100 g (3½ oz) polyunsaturated margarine,	and stoned
melted	25 g (1 oz) milk chocolate chips
1 egg	

1. Preheat the oven to Gas Mark 4/180°C/fan oven 160°C. Line a 20 cm (8 inch) square tin with non stick baking parchment.

2. Sift the flour and cocoa powder into a mixing bowl and stir in the sugar.

3. Pour the margarine over the dry ingredients along with the egg, milk and almond essence, and mix to a soft batter. Fold in the cherries and chocolate chips.

4. Pour the mixture into the prepared tin and bake for 25 minutes. Allow it to cool in the tin for 15 minutes and then carefully transfer it to a wire rack to cool completely. Cut it into 12 brownies.

tip: *Brownies are meant to have a soft, chewy texture, so take care not to over bake them. They will appear a little soft to the touch after 25 minutes baking, but they will firm up on cooling.*

4 POINTS

Tropical celebration cake

79 Points per recipe | Takes 45 minutes to prepare, 2½ hours to bake + 30 minutes standing + cooling overnight

V *Makes 20 slices. Calories per serving 255. Freeze ✗*

Whether for Christmas, Easter or birthday celebrations, a cake is always appreciated.

---

low fat cooking spray

225 g (8 oz) sultanas

4 tablespoons brandy

100 g (3½ oz) ready to eat dried apricots, diced

100 g (3½ oz) glacé cherries, chopped roughly

100 g (3½ oz) glacé pineapple, diced roughly

50 g (1¾ oz) stem ginger, chopped finely

75 g (2¾ oz) dried apple rings, chopped roughly

50 g (1¾ oz) pecan nuts, chopped

finely grated zest and juice of 1 orange

finely grated zest of 1 lemon

100 g (3½ oz) polyunsaturated margarine

100 g (3½ oz) soft dark brown sugar

4 eggs

200 g (7 oz) plain white flour

a pinch of salt

3 teaspoons ground mixed spice

To decorate:

2 tablespoons reduced sugar apricot jam

225 g (8 oz) ready to roll white fondant icing

length of coloured ribbon

---

1. Lightly spray a 20 cm (8 inch) round cake tin with low fat cooking spray. Line the base and sides with non stick baking parchment.

2. Place the sultanas in a mixing bowl with the brandy, apricots, glacé cherries, glacé pineapple, ginger and apple rings. Stir well and leave to stand for 30 minutes.

3. Mix in the nuts, orange zest and juice and lemon zest to the fruit mixture. Preheat the oven to Gas Mark 2/150°C/fan oven 130°C. Beat together the margarine and sugar until fluffy, and add the eggs one at a time, whisking well after each one. Sift in the flour and fold it into the mixture with the salt and mixed spice.

4. Add the fruit and nut mixture to the flour and egg mixture and stir well. Spoon it all into the prepared tin and level the top with the back of a spoon. Bake in the oven for 2½ hours.

5. Carefully remove the cake from the tin and allow it to cool completely on a wire rack – it's best to leave it overnight, covered with a clean tea towel.

6. To decorate the cake, warm the apricot jam and brush it over the top and sides of the cake. Roll out the fondant icing on a clean surface and use it to cover the cake, pressing it down well with your hands. Place the cake on a cake board and tie a coloured ribbon around it. Re-roll any fondant trimmings and cut out shapes to decorate the top depending on the occasion, for example, make stars or bells for Christmas.

tip: To check if the cake is cooked or not, insert a metal skewer into the centre of the cake, count to five and then remove the skewer. If the skewer comes out clean, the cake is cooked. If any mixture sticks to the skewer, return it to the oven until it is cooked.